NEW WORLDS OF OCEANOGRAPHY

is a fascinating exploration into tomorrow's knowledge of the wealth of the sea.

NEW WORLDS OF OCEANOGRAPHY

documents America's billion-dollar development of the ocean's treasure and its limitless supply of natural resources in the years to come.

NEW WORLDS OF OCEANOGRAPHY

tells us how—

- we can mine a cubic mile of sea-water containing 18 million tons of magnesium and 25 tons of gold
- we can find new deep underwater treasure worth countless billions of dollars in the next five years
- we can desalt enough drinking water from the sea to serve the needs of every person in the world a thousand times over
- we will use "oceanic engineering" to secure the great fishing catch in our seven seas

NEW WORLDS OF OCEANOGRAPHY

captures all of the color, excitement and potential of the sea and its occupants.

ABOUT THE AUTHOR

Captain Long's interest in the sea goes back to his boyhood and family jaunts to the seashore. His first scientific closeup of oceanography came in 1934 when he became a staff member of the National Geographic-New York Zoological bathysphere expedition in Bermuda, under Dr. William Beebe.

In World War II with the U.S. Navy, he observed the atolls and shells of Micronesia in the mid-Pacific, during off-duty hours. A founder-trustee of the International Oceanographic Foundation, he was associate editor of its magazine *Sea Frontiers*, for four years; he has edited the symposium *Ocean Sciences*, a book on oceanography for the U.S. Naval Institute at Annapolis; he is the author of a brochure, *Opportunities in Oceanography*, for the Smithsonian Institute. Recently, he has become publisher of *Ocean Science News* and one of the editors of *Geo-Marine Technology*, a new monthly oceanographic magazine, both of Washington, D.C.

THE WORLDS OF SCIENCE OCEANOGRAPHY

NEW WORLDS OF OCEANOGRAPHY

CAPTAIN E. JOHN LONG, USNR (ret)

Preface by
SENATOR WARREN G. MAGNUSON

PYRAMID PUBLICATONS • NEW YORK

For

Virginia and Jessica

NEW WORLDS OF OCEANOGRAPHY

A WORLDS OF SCIENCE BOOK

First printing, September 1965
second printing, April 1966

Copyright © 1965 by E. John Long

All Rights Reserved

Printed in the United States of America

WORLDS OF SCIENCE BOOKS are published by Pyramid Publications, Inc.
444 Madison Avenue, New York, New York 10022, U.S.A.

CONTENTS

		Pages
Introduction		7
Foreword		9
Preface		12
Chapter I	Realm of "Living Fossils"	19
Chapter II	Man and the Sea	34
Chapter III	Currents, Waves, and the Like	56
Chapter IV	The Living Waters—Fishes and Mammals	72
Chapter V	The Bottom—and Lower	91
Chapter VI	Most Precious Mineral—And Others	111
Chapter VII	Poisoning the Sea	126
Chapter VIII	Birthplace of Storms	136
Chapter IX	Making Fisheries Pay	150
Chapter X	Gadgets and Hardware	169
Chapter XI	Oceanic Defense Problems	182
Chapter XII	A Glimpse Into the Future	193

INTRODUCTION
A Burgeoning New Science

Just what is oceanography? What does the word mean? Unless your dictionary is very new, it may dismiss oceanography as "geography that deals with the ocean and its phenomena."

Yet even the novice in science knows that modern oceanography is concerned with much more range than the sea. It is obvious that this new realm of research is extending deep into the ocean, is exploring the sea bottom, and is beginning to penetrate the core structure of the land beneath the ocean floor. Furthermore, oceanographers have become aware of a growing kinship of the sea with the atmosphere above the surface, and even the part that weather satellites are playing in hurricanes and typhoons—all of which are knitted into the fabric of modern oceanography.

In other words, oceanography has become a vast assembly of related activities without yet acquiring formal status in academic circles as a separate scientific discipline under its own name. The best definition that the academicians will grant to it is that oceanography is a congeries, or mixture, of several disciplines. The National Academy of Sciences tucks it away among "the earth sciences." A well-wisher has suggested that, in its now expanded image, "oceanography" should be replaced by a formerly established name, "oceanology," now listed as obsolete.

But oceanography has grown so suddenly and expanded so rapidly that any change in name for it at this late date would be most difficult if not impossible to make. Anyway, there is no valid reason why the term "oceanography" cannot go right on as it is, forgetting about disciplines, or congeries, or any other umbrella-word. While to the purists "oceanography" may be an orphan term, time and usage should make its overall function familiar.

Meanwhile, let us pioneer in a venture in marine nomenclature and sanction the use of oceanography's shorter brother "oceanic." For the purpose of this book, there-

8 • NEW WORLDS OF OCEANOGRAPHY

fore, the two words shall be synonymous terms—and may the flotsam and jetsam fall where they may!

How much area does this vast new operation, known as oceanography, encompass? It includes a multitude of things, some of them overlapping and interrelated, but the field is usually subdivided into ocean engineering and four major research areas: (1) physical, (2) chemical, (3) geological, and (4) biological.

Only by studying all these fields of ocean science can we understand and be able to predict the ways of the sea and its creatures. The need for scientists today is not just for specialists in one of these areas, but for those who can be knowledgeable in two or more of them. Also needed are scientists who bring to oceanography the skills of other branches of knowledge, such as meteorology and nuclear physics.

Primarily, however, is the need for men trained in the four major research areas:

(1) *Physical.* Currents, waves, temperatures, tides, weather influence, interface (boundary between sea and air), density of water, thermal gradients (heat distribution in the sea), thermoclines, transmission of sound and underseas communication, extraction of power from the sea, weather satellites.

(2) *Chemical.* Salinity, minerals in solution, corrosion, pollution, minute elements (may be useful in design and operation of future sea farms), and extraction of minerals from the water.

(3) *Geological.* Bottom topography, earth's magnetic field, natural and man-induced seismic or earthquake activity, heat transference from earth's interior, mineral contents of silt and rock strata, mineral nodules on ocean floor, reefs, fossils, cores, and oil and sulfur deposits in the sea.

(4) *Biological.* Plants and animals living in sea, from bacteria and minute phytoplankton (tiny one-cell plants which drift at the mercy of currents), to the blue whale, largest living creature. Productivity of sea, marine food resources, production of light and electricity by marine animals, scattering layers, fouling and corrosion of organisms, effects of radio-

activity on marine plants and animals, and identification of all species of marine life.

In meeting the long-range goals needed by oceanography's rapid growth, many military and civilian government agencies and private commercial concerns will be needed, not only for ships, instruments, and supplies, but also, more important, for highly trained scientists. Now that we realize that the nation's future, in fact its very survival, may depend upon our knowledge of the sea, we must keep pace with the growing demand for research talent and especially for student supporting staffs in the marine sciences.

If this book has a mission, let it be to inspire young people, both men and women, with a "feeling for the sea," so that oceanography may play its big and important role in the advancement of the nation.

E. J. L.

FOREWORD

"The seas around us . . . represent one of our most important resources. If vigorously developed, this resource can be a source of great benefit to the Nation and to all mankind. But it will require concerted action, purposefully directed, with vision and ingenuity. It will require the combined efforts of our scientists and institutions, both public and private, and the coordinated efforts of many Federal agencies. . . .

"Knowledge of the oceans is more than a matter of curiosity. Our very survival may hinge upon it. Although understanding of our marine environment and maps of the ocean floor would afford to our military forces a demonstrable advantage, we have thus far neglected oceanography. We do not have adequate charts of more than one or two percent of the oceans.

"The seas also offer a wealth of nutritional resources. They already are a principal source of protein. They can provide many times the current food supply if we but learn how to garner and husband this self-renewing larder. To meet the vast needs of an expanding population, the bounty of the sea must be made more available. Within two decades, our own Nation will require over a million more tons of seafood than we now harvest.

"Mineral resources on land will ultimately reach their limits. But the oceans hold untapped sources of such basic minerals as salt, potassium and magnesium, in virtually limitless quantities. We shall be able to extract additional elements from sea water, such as manganese, nickel, cobalt and others known to abound on the ocean floor, as soon as the processes are developed to make it economically feasible.

"To predict, and perhaps some day to control, changes in weather and climate is of the utmost importance to man everywhere. These changes are controlled to a large and yet unknown extent by what happens in the ocean.

Ocean and atmosphere work together in a still mysterious way to determine our climate. Additional research is necessary to identify the factors in this interplay.

"These are some of the reasons which compel us to embark upon a national effort in oceanography...."

PRESIDENT JOHN F. KENNEDY,
Message to the Congress on Oceanography
(*Executive Communication No. 734*

March 29, 1961

PREFACE
by
WARREN G. MAGNUSON
U.S. Senator from Washington
Chairman, Commerce Committee, U.S. Senate*

The seas are many things to many men. To some they are vast arenas of adventure. To others they spell rest or romance. To still others they seem a blue-green waste, while there are those who dread them as a scourge of storms and hurricanes.

Some look on the oceans mainly as highways of international commerce; others as war theaters fading into history. To scientists they are immense hydrological laboratories occupying, with their adjacent sea areas, 137 million square miles or 71 percent of the earth's surface. In fact, the water volume of the seas is eight times that of all land above them, and the sea contains physical phenomena and complex forms of life as yet unknown.

The seas stir man and shape his destiny in different ways, but to all people in all ages they have held in their dark depths multitudes of mysteries. Nations and scientists in this scientific era have sought to unlock some of these age-old secrets and with some—but never complete—success; yet many, too many, mysteries of the oceans, as Captain Long so ably outlines in his fascinating book, remain.

Thus the seas present an enormous challenge to science, to students and others who will be scientists and technolo-

* Senator Magnuson introduced the original legislation which now enables the U. S. Coast Guard, Coast and Geodetic Survey and U. S. Geological Survey to engage in ocean-wide research, and the Senate Resolution officially commending the report and recommendations of the Committee on Oceanography of the National Academy of Sciences—National Research Council. His bills embodying the Committee's proposals and authorizing a 10-year comprehensive national oceanographic program passed the U. S. Senate in both the 86th and 87th Congress but were not approved by the House of Representatives. Senator Magnuson is still championing a greatly expanded marine research and survey program.

gists of the future, and to the governments of nations in which these potential scientists and engineers are planning their careers.

Governments can, of course, accept or reject and ignore this challenge. They may accept with enthusiasm and energy and meet this challenge broadly, or they can accept it halfheartedly with reservations coupled with dispersed and tardy effort. Whatever action is taken, governments are confronted with this challenge; insofar as our own nation is concerned, the challenge of the oceans is as urgent as that of space.

Space is visible; the seas only a few feet below the surface are not. Utilizing the electromagnetic spectrum man has learned to transmit and receive communications through space. His ability to do so through the ocean depths is limited.

Space, like the oceans, is owned by no one; but the oceans in one sense are owned by everyone. The high seas are open to the craft of the world. Their resources are available to whomever has the capability of locating and harvesting them.

Space is infinite. The oceans are earth's own. No other planet in our solar system has them and for that reason it can be assumed that none supports life like our own.

Space is so vast; its conquest so costly, that it is improbable that another nation may gain domination over it and by such domination rule the world. But it is not improbable that another nation, and with far less cost and effort, could attain control of the world ocean if we stand idly by, and there is reason to suspect that one nation, the U.S.S.R., has precisely that object in mind.

Soviet Russia has more submarines than all the nations of the Free World, more minelayers and minesweepers than any other navy, and its naval aircraft, I am told, outnumber our own.

Soviet Russia has more oceanographic research and survey ships than the combined nations of the Free World. Moreover, it has the largest and most diversified oceanographic vessels, has more scientists serving at sea than any other nation, and is conducting ocean-wide scientific work in the Atlantic, Pacific, Indian, Arctic, and Antarctic.

Soviet Russia has the world's most efficient fishing fleets.

In these fleets are the world's largest fishery vessels, factory ships, mother ships, refrigerated craft and giant stern ramp trawlers (we have none) all potentially useful as Soviet Navy Auxiliaries—and experts believe they are being so used now. These ships carry not only marine scientists but navy hydrographic officers trained in intelligence and electronic techniques. Soviet trawlers snooping along our coasts have sophisticated instruments that bear little or no re-relation to fisheries exploration, but marked relation to naval reconnaissance, which can be conducted while the fishermen on the ships compete for the food riches of the seas.

Soviet Russia has massed as many as 200 fishing vessels large and small at one time on Georges Bank off New England and has simultaneously sent trawlers to scout the length of our Atlantic Coast from Long Island to Florida. Two years ago, Russia had five large refrigerated trawlers operating out of Cuba, and is building a port ample to accommodate many more.

In the North Pacific more than 200 Russian vessels, including factory ships and stern ramp trawlers, have been operating in the Gulf of Alaska and the Bering Sea. Translations from Russian scientific journals indicate that the U.S.S.R. is contemplating extensive tuna fisheries in subtropical areas of both the Pacific and Atlantic, with a fleet of tuna clippers now under construction.

The magazine *Navy*, in a recent issue, reported that 500 Soviet naval officers have been specially trained for intelligence work on Soviet fishing vessels, tankers, freighters, and passenger ships equipped with advanced oceanographic instruments.

This activity is, of course, in addition to that of its huge, modern oceanographic fleet in which at least some ships carry a plaque bearing the likeness of Lenin with this quotation:

> In order to spread world communism, it is necessary to use the fields of science and technology.

So the challenge is not new. It dates back to the man who masterminded the Russian Revolution and who brought so much misery on the world. It is a challenge that applies equally to the oceans and to space, although the Russians have chosen to emphasize their achievements in the latter.

"Can this be a ruse?" the president of one of our major civilian research institutes asked during a seminar of scientists. He continued:

"The Russians boast about their missiles and their 100 megaton bombs; they are very quiet about their submarines. They make a lot of noise about their men in space; they are very quiet about an effort in oceanography several times as large as ours. What a brilliant military exploit it would be to send us off to the moon while they seize the ocean."

Our national interest, indeed our national survival, demands that no foreign power gain dominion either of the oceans or in space. Recently in advocating a national 10-year oceanographic program, I stated that if the U.S.S.R. succeeds in ruling the waves, and the waters beneath, it will control 90 percent of earth's surface and imperil the remaining 10 percent with ballistic missiles fired from submarines hovering along the continental shelves. I see no reason to modify that statement now.

The prevention of Communist domination of the seas is perhaps our most pressing problem today. In its famous summary report, the Committee of Oceanography stated without equivocation:

> From the point of view of military operations there is no comparison between the urgencies of the problems of the oceans and those of outer space. The submarine armed with long range missiles, is probably the most potent weapon system threatening our security today.

Yet our oceanographic research program has lagged, and continues to lag today. The 1965 budget, for example, called for appropriations to continue our expensive explorations in *space*, which are many times greater than those for marine research and surveys.

No nation is more vulnerable to attack from the sea than the United States, and no nation would suffer as heavy material loss from such attack as ours.

The United States has a continental coastline of 11,633 miles. Our island state of Hawaii has a 750-mile coastline, while our territories and possessions have a combined coastline 673 miles long. Thus our coastline, totaling 13,056 miles, is the second longest of any country in the world, exceeded, in fact, only by that of Canada. More than half of Canada's coastline is in the icebound Arctic. So, in fact, the United States may be considered to have the longest useful coastline.

Even the Arctic no longer can be considered a barrier to naval operations, however, as was pointed out recently by H. B. Hachey, Chief Oceanographer for Canada's Fisheries Research Board. Dr. Hachey said:

> "Until recent years the North American Continent, relatively untouched by modern wars, was looked upon as a bastion, well removed and protected from warring nations by the oceans on three coasts. In particular, the Arctic Coast could be forgotten because of the difficulties of operation. Navigation under the Arctic ice by atomic-powered submarines has now been shown to be feasible. This in itself has opened up a host of problems relating to defence. Methods of detecting the modern submarine are much more involved than heretofore, and a very technical knowledge of the ocean itself is required for efficient application of modern defence methods."

In the United States 9 of our 10 largest cities, 15 of our top 20, are open to attack by ocean carriers, and one sixth of all the world's international commerce passes through American ports.

America's economy, welfare, and security are dependent on freedom of the seas, a freedom that is progressively being challenged.

What is to be done about it?

The immediate and most pressing need as I see it is to train more oceanographers, more marine biologists, more marine chemists, more marine geologists, more geophysical oceanographers, more experts in every field of science and engineering that relates to the seas.

Research ships and marine laboratory facilities are needed, too, but only as fast as we have the scientific and technological manpower to make full and effective use of them.

The late President Kennedy expressed the need better in a message to Congress in which he stated: "The most important part of our long range program in oceanography is the training of young scientists."

Soviet Russia has approximately 60 percent more professional oceanographers than the United States, and is training many hundreds of selected students in the marine sciences.

So again we are faced by a challenge, or rather a group of challenges, the challenge to educate and train more of our young people in this vital and crucial scientific field, the challenge to provide facilities where they may acquire this training, the challenge to assist those students who show most promise by advancing their training, and the challenge to interest young people in acquiring such training.

This is where Captain Long's book has particular value. His chapter headings such as "Realm of Living Fossils," "Poisoning the Sea," "Birthplace of Storms," and "Men and the Sea" should stimulate many to greater interest in the oceans.

Captain Long throughout his lifetime has been fascinated by the oceans and was among the pioneers in modern ocean research. In 1934 he was a staff member of the National Geographic-William Beebe bathysphere expedition off Bermuda. During World War II he served as a Navy officer in both the Atlantic and Pacific. Immediately after the war he was aide to Secretary of Defense James Forrestal and served on the staff of the U.S. Naval Academy.

In recent years Captain Long has been a contributing editor of *Sea Frontiers,* the quarterly magazine of the International Oceanographic Foundation. He is at present publisher of *Ocean Science News,* a Washington newsletter.

It is Captain Long's conviction, in which I share, that throughout the nation there is a tremendous latent interest in the oceans, an interest which will require little to awaken.

The seas are a part of our heritage. They have been and are a major physical factor in our national life and culture, and in that of the New World. For four centuries they were for millions the way of escape from Old World dynastic and religious quarrels, social injustice, economic hardship, or tyranny. Men and women and their families crossed the oceans to seek and find a new life in a new land, a life of freedom and opportunity.

During the first three of these four centuries the seas were also the cruel routes over which thousands were brought to this hemisphere as slaves, but their descendants, too, have found increasing opportunity and justice. It is in the Old World, behind the Iron Curtain, that human beings in this century have lost their freedom.

The nations which have destroyed freedom in this generation seek to extend their system across the oceans to this hemisphere, to the islands and the continent in the Pacific, to every land and every people not presently under the Red flag, regardless of what expanses of ocean may lie between. This is the immediate challenge our marine scientists can and must help us meet.

CHAPTER I

REALM OF "LIVING FOSSILS"

"Beginnings are apt to be shadowy, and so it is with the beginnings of that great mother of life, the sea."
THE SEA AROUND US, Rachel L. Carson (Oxford)

SCIENTISTS ARE GENERALLY AGREED now that all life on earth began in the sea. With pardonable pride, therefore, the oceanographer can claim that his work runs back to the very beginnings of activity on the planet, when steaming clouds of vapor concealed its still heated exterior. Many, many eons later the outer crust gradually cooled, and finally water settled into the earth pattern we know today—almost three quarters sea, and the rest land.

Somewhere during this interminable geological time many forms of life must have emerged, some of them by blending with each other, and others by defying the shifting patterns of evolution. But how did the elements themselves produce the organic compounds from which all life came into existence? While this is the supreme mystery of the universe, there is no lack of theories or conjecture about it.

The first earth rain, condensing from materials created by immense meteorites, must have been rich in scores of liquids as well as solid compounds. Among the ingredients, perhaps, were amino acids, the building blocks of living protein, which experimenters have produced by shooting electric charges and ultraviolet or other rays through artificial atmosphere.

No "Flying Saucers"

Although such an idea seems a bit primitive, and perhaps is over-simplified, it is certainly more palatable than such notions as "flying saucers" and their little men from Mars, or such similar figments of the imagination. Sometimes, for security reasons, certain odd land and sea discoveries have been concealed and even denied, but eventually most of them have been disclosed as natural phenomena and the rest will probably be unveiled as being of similar origin.

Whatever the source of biological life on this planet, it can be reasonably assumed that it originated in the sea, moving gradually up to land through the ocean shallows. This seems more logical than land forms reverting to the sea, because every major species known to man is contained in the oceans. Some of these forms of life have remained in the sea; a few of them changing little from their earliest ancestors.

Oldest Inhabitant

Take for instance the familiar horseshoe crab, which is not a "crab" at all, but rather a distant sea predecessor of land spiders and scorpions. Its closest zoological kinship is with the long extinct tribolites, which flourished during the dim mists and eternal rains of the Cambrian period, 300 million years ago, the oldest period known to sustain life.

With the exception of a handful of small marine organisms, the horseshoe crab—known more formally as *Limulus polyphemus*—is the world's oldest *surviving* inhabitant! A genuine "living fossil" and a zoological curiosity, it has two distinct pair of eyes, one a compound, many-lensed type, and the other small and simple. The compound eye similar to the eyes of bees, and, with it, *Limulus* can see polarized light rays, even ultraviolet and infrared, which are invisible to humans.

What a pity that *Limulus*, whose relatives are very scarce and who is much pampered in aquariums in Europe, receives such scant respect in the New World. In fact, a sizeable industry has sprung up in Delaware Bay, where horseshoe crabs are netted in vast numbers and are ground up for fertilizer and for hog and poultry feed.

Living Fossil Returns

Because rapid evolution is not encouraged nor developed in the relatively stable environment of the sea, it is possible for creatures known only as fossils on land to remain as living links in the ocean depths. Take the *coelacanth* (pronounced "seé-la-canth") for instance, a fish believed to have vanished completely from the world more than 50 million years ago—until one of them showed up *very much alive* in the net of an Indian Ocean ship, December 22, 1938!

A total of 27 specimens of the big fish (it grows up to 5 feet long and attains a weight of 150 pounds) have since been found in the same Indian Ocean area, proving that this discovery was not a complete freak. None remained alive long, but most of the specimens have been preserved or mounted. An excellent replica can be found at the Smithsonian Institution in Washington, D.C. A specimen is preserved in formalin at Rhodes University College in Grahamstown, South Africa. Another is at the American Muséum of Natural History, New York, and several can be observed at the Museum National d'Histoire Naturelle in Paris.

Withholds Sea Secrets

This incredible creature, which startled science and sent a wave of amazement around the oceanographic world a quarter of a century ago, has raised a number of old questions about evolution and the survival of the species. Once again it proved that secrets can be kept easier in the sea than on land and that we are more likely to learn more new things there than anywhere else.

The coelacanth is not a pretty fellow. In fact, it looks a bit lumpy and misshapen, with its snapping predatory jaws, its flashing greenish-yellow eyes and its overlapping scales, the color of a steel-blue watch spring. But the most striking of its features are the dorsal and pectoral fins. These are set on peduncles, or stalks resembling vestigial limbs, as if it had emerged or expected some day to emerge from the water and walk on shore. Its spine, a tube of cartilage, protrudes between the main lobes of the tail like an auxiliary tail. This was noticed by Louis Agassiz in its *fossil form*, and led him to classify the coelacanths as a heretofore unknown family, even as early as the 1830's.

If all of this seems to be giving too much attention to

one creature, it should be remembered that coelacanths developed during the reign of the tribolites, who dominated life for 75 times as long as man has been on earth. The coelacanths were alive during the comparatively short period of the dinosaurs, and of the passing of the saber-toothed tiger, the dodo, and scores of others. Fossil deposits of them have been found in Europe, Greenland, and several parts of the United States, including the excavated site of the University Library, in Princeton, New Jersey.

Discovered by a Woman

Discovery of the first specimen of a live coelacanth is a story almost as amazing as the examination of the fish itself. It proves that an oceanographer must keep alert to everything that takes place in or comes from the sea and must never take anything for granted. In the finding of the coelacanth, the story begins on the municipal wharf of East London, South Africa, in 1938. Miss M. Courtenay-Latimer, the young curator of the East London Museum, was watching the unloading of sharks from the trawler *Nerine* when one curious specimen caught her eye. It was not a shark; in fact, she admitted she did not know what it was. But she induced a taxi driver to haul the 127-pound creature—by this time dead and highly odoriferous—to the museum.

In high excitement she photographed it (none of the pictures came out), and drew some sketches, before turning the fish over to a taxidermist. The sketches and a letter went forward to her friend Professor J. L. B. Smith, a chemistry instructor at nearby Grahamstown. As South Africa's leading part-time ichthyologist, he was interested, but dubious. He wrote: "It is curious that in spite of all this evidence, my intellect says that such things can't happen." But he hastened over to East London.

"That first sight hit me like a white-hot blast," he admitted, "and made me feel shaky and queer; my body tingled! I stood as if stricken to stone. Yes, there was not the shadow of a doubt, scale by scale, fin by fin, it was a true coelacanth."

Was It a Stray?

When he had caught his breath, Dr. Smith named it *Latimeria chalumnae*, in honor of the young woman curator and to note that the fish was caught near the mouth of the Chalumna River. Was it a stray from distant depths or were there others nearby which had been overlooked by simple fishermen? Smith, now emboldened, predicted that others would be found in areas off South Africa, Mozambique, and the waters around Madagascar (now the Malagasy Republic).

But although he printed descriptions of the fish far and wide in French, Portuguese, and English and offered a reward for it, 14 long years passed before the Professor's promise to locate "Old Fourlegs" again came true, in a region he had predicted, the Comoros, in the Mozambique Channel.

Although it has been misrepresented as a "missing link" between sea and land creatures, the coelacanth, most paleontologists now agree, must be regarded as a remarkable exception from the general rule that appears to have governed the evolution, rise and fall of species generally. The major thing we have learned from it, according to Professor Smith, is that "of all types of animals that have been evolved, it retained primitive characteristics the longest and . . . endured almost unchanged over an unusually long stretch of time."

To a woman acquaintance who did not like the idea of being a descendant of the ugly creature, Dr. Smith replied with a wry grin that a coelacanth is "only a cousin of an ancestor." Technically, it is related collaterally to the Rhipidistia, or fringe-fanned fish, which may have come out of remote sea swamps, possibly linking marine life to amphibia and mammals. However, there is no direct bridge between the coelacanth and Rhipidistia. Let us leave it that the coelacanth "just wants to be alone."

Shark An Oldtimer

Although not exactly a fossil, the shark has been with us for a long, long time. Its ancestors date back about 350 million years, to the upper Devonian geological period, when it first appeared as a shark-like animal, the *cladose-*

24 • NEW WORLDS OF OCEANOGRAPHY

lache. They appear to be the nearest biological approach to "perpetual motion," at least in the animal kingdom. Sharks must remain swimming all the time, night and day, from birth to death, because they do not have skin bladders like most other fish, which would enable them to float when weary.

Like a fossil, the shark has retained through the ages several points that are different from other fishes. For example, the fins of a shark, other than the caudal (tail) fin, are not as flexible as those of bony fishes and cannot be utilized for forward propulsion, according to Dr. Paul W. Hess, of the University of Delaware. They can only guide the animal after a forward thrust that seems primarily to be a side-to-side motion of the caudal fin. The fin structure, therefore, dictates that the shark cannot back down once it has overshot its target. It must swing out and make a new approach, following a typical figure eight while searching or feeding.

Tribolites, a Strange Tribe

Of all sea fossils, the strangest is the tribolite, ancestrally related perhaps to insects, spiders, crabs, and lobsters. For more than 150 million years the tribolites were earth's dominant animals, enjoying life in warm shallow seas and defending themselves by rolling up into balls whose bristling spikes must have made them difficult for others to eat. Some species of these odd creatures may have lived partially buried in the bottom sediment, where their projecting or stalked eyes enabled them to detect any nearby movement. Sea vegetation, clusters of other marine animals such as sea lilites, and crannies in reefs would have afforded places of concealment—for in this era the defender rather than the aggressor won.

Then came the vertebrates and other more advanced forms of life, and about 250 million years ago the tribolites disappeared completely. Why did such a fate (extinction) overcome a group of animals that, for millions of years, were well adapted to their surroundings and continued to evolve new species? According to Dr. H. B. Whittington, a professor of geology at Harvard University, the fierce competition with other groups for food may have played a part in the tribolites' demise. In addition, fishes, among which jaws evolved for the first time, may have become tribolite predators. Larger and more powerful animals, such as the nautiloids, ancestors of the modern nautilus, had grasping tentacles and powerful jaws. They could have seized and eaten tribolites.

A Mystery of Evolution

But no one knows for sure why the tribolites disappeared so abruptly after their long dominance. The pat answer is that eventually the rate of extinction became greater than the rate of evolution—which tells us little that we did not already know. Chalk up the tribolites as one of the mysteries of evolution for future reference and solution.

So much for a host of "fossils" living and dead. What about their environment, as the sea level has risen and fallen, and the continents themselves have been on the move? A new science of paleomagnetism is reviving the old theory that the world's continents were once joined together in one original land mass that finally split up and slowly drifted apart.

Suppose we take the continental drift theory first, and then consider the vagaries of sea levels. Dr. Alfred Wegener, a German meteorologist, noted that the opposing shores of the North and South Atlantic had a complimentary look on a globe. He was not the first to notice this, but he went further to delve into the geology of adjacent regions. He came up with rocks and at least one organism (the fossil reptile Mesocaurus) that were found nowhere except in South Africa and Brazil. Wegener found other areas that would fit into his theoretical jigsaw, including geological formations in North America that would match up with those of the British Isles and Scandinavia.

What Force Strong Enough?

Geologists as a whole were skeptical about Wegener's notion. What forces within the earth were powerful enough to move solid continents large distances, let alone split them into fragments? But a half century later, the

26 • NEW WORLDS OF OCEANOGRAPHY

Wegener theory, which was independently advanced at about the same time by the American scientist, F. B. Taylor, was revived and updated by new scientific findings. In fact, there is evidence that North America is still drifting about 1/3 of an inch westward, away from Europe, every year. A team of three Australian scientists also has concluded that Australia has drifted north from Antarctica some 3,400 miles in 100 million years, at an average speed of about 2 inches a year.

Magnetism in ancient rocks is now interpreted as evidence that the southern continents were once clustered together. The earth's molten iron core, gradually increasing in size about 200 million years ago, gave rise to giant whirlpools of heat that began to move the continents apart, a perceptible drift still in progress.

"Fixed Compasses"

Now comes S. K. Runcorn, of the University of Durham, England, who further supports the theory of continental drift and adds to it a contentious theory that the earth was formed "cold" about 4.5 billion years ago. Runcorn expands on the Wegener thesis of continental drift, basing his theory largely on fossils, geology, and geography, and certain lavas and sandstones which have retained a record of the earth's magnetic field at the time these fossils were laid down.

In a way, these magnetic fossils constitute "fixed compasses," determining where north was in ancient times. By studying these magnetic fossils, Runcorn and others have found that the continents have altered their position relative to one another and relative to the north and south poles. Thus essentially, Wegener was correct. Convection currents, which carry heat to just beneath the earth's surface, have also been responsible for moving continents thousands of miles across the earth's surface.

A footnote in passing: Wegener even had names for two of the protocontinents. North America and Europe he called "Lauasia" and all the other continents, as they are known today, Wegener grouped into the second great land mass, which he called "Gonwandaland." The seas around them are not listed.

Did Earth Form "Cold"?

Runcorn's other theory, about the earth forming "cold," has not received as much welcome among scientists. But in case that he, too, might be ahead of the times, let us report it in essence:

> The earth formed cold out of iron and stony meteorites some 4.5 billion years ago. In time, radio-active processes began to melt the iron, which settled to the center of the earth. About 3 billion years ago the core began to grow, as more iron settled in the molten core. As the core grew the pattern of convection currents changed. But it was not until about 200 million years ago that the core reached the critical size which changed the convection current pattern in such a way that it altered the distribution of the continents and set them adrift.

If Runcorn's theory is right, it means that upheavals in the earth's land masses are a relatively recent thing. Here Runcorn runs head-on into the opinions of many scientists, who still hold that the earth formed from space as a molten mass that has cooled off slowly at the surface, only after many millions of years.

Rugged Primordial Crust

For many years scientists have wondered what the *original surface* of the earth was like before the rains came and covered much of the ocean floor with blankets of sediment. Did large meteors and other objects that rained on the earth produce giant craters like those that still pock the rainless lunar landscape? Or did the earth's jagged appearance result from the final agony of volcanoes and other upheavals before the earth more or less solidified from its molten state?

Experts still do not know the answers to these questions but they have advanced a step toward solving them. In brief, this has been done by using a technique that can chart contours of the earth's apparent original crust far beneath the sediment layers. The technique and its results were presented recently by Dr. Maurice Ewing, director of Columbia University's Lamont Geological Observatory, his brother Dr. John L. Ewing, and their co-workers. The method is analogous to that of the conventional echo-sounder used on ships.

28 • NEW WORLDS OF OCEANOGRAPHY

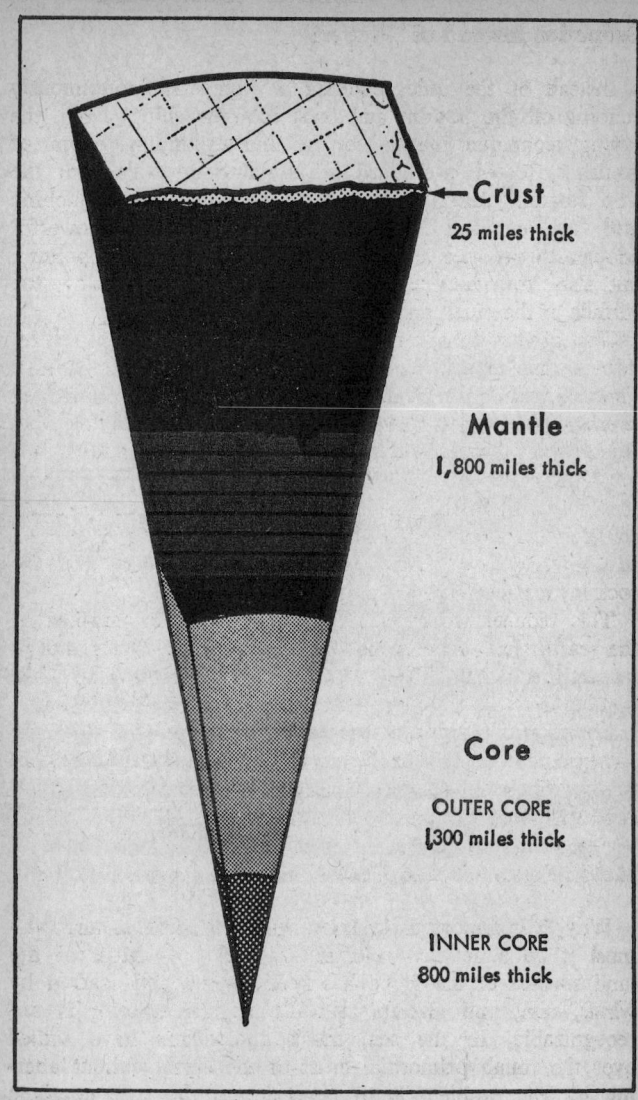

Total Structure of the Earth

(National Science Foundation)

Grenades Instead of "Pingers"

Instead of the quiet clicking of "pingers," continuously echoing off the bottom and back into the ship's cabin, the Ewing technique makes use of the resounding boom of grenades, tossed overboard at 2-minute intervals with the ship steaming at 10 knots. With a good baseball-pitching arm, the operator can thus obtain an explosion powerful enough to produce echoes, not only from the sea bottom, but also from rock layers as much as 3 miles below the surface of the muck and sand.

The observations are carried out around the clock by three 4-man teams. When a timer, set to buzz at 2-minute intervals, sounds, the charge, its fuse lighted, is tossed well overboard. At the same time a hydrophone, trailing 150 feet astern, is released. After about 10 seconds the hydrophone is reeled in and preparations are made for the next shot. Returning signals, like those on an ordinary echo-sounder, are recorded on a moving roll of paper, which shows both the profile of the ocean's floor debris and the rock layer beneath it.

This pioneer work on the original moon-like surface of the earth has been done by the Lamont Observatory's research schooner *Vema* on two recent around-the-world cruises. But the equipment has also been used on cooperating Argentine ships as part of an intensive study of the Argentine Basin, a little known area embracing a million square miles to the east of South America in the South Atlantic Ocean.

Must Be Done At Sea Only

Why is it important to know such phenomena, and why must it be done at sea instead of on land? Most of the land surface of the globe has been eroded and scarred by winds, rain, and glaciers until its original exterior is unrecognizable. In the sea, muck and debris have settled over the rough primordial crust of the earth without altering it. The problem is to penetrate to the true contours through the light and heavy sediments.

While the Ewing technique can give only approximate depths of the sediments, because of the uncertainty as to the travel time of sound through the various materials, it nevertheless will further illuminate the history of our planet, show how its continents and oceans were formed, whether the continents continuously change their relative positions, and perhaps even how the ice ages came about.

Dr. Ewing believes that the idea of continental drift should be given a fair test, but he believes the distribution of sediments, when further explored and contacted on the floors of all oceans, may contradict it. More midocean drilling techniques and more core samples must be put to use, marine geologists agree, not only to explore some of the "missing" sediments and other ocean-bottom puzzles, but also to achieve that ultimate geological-marine goal, known as the Mohole Project (see Chapter V).

Is Sea All "Ups"?

While the seas may be preserving the original crust of the earth, sea level itself has been having its ups and downs over the last 6,000 years, fluctuating from about 5 feet below to 10 feet above the present sea level. At least this is the theory of most textbooks today. Recently Dr. Francis P. Shepard, an oceanographer with the Scripps Institution of Oceanography, in the authoritative *Journal of Science,* has advanced some rather convincing new evidence. He claims that sea level has been going up and up, with very little down. According to his conclusions, based on the dating of shells and other records now submerged, the oceans have risen roughly 20 feet during the past 6,000 years, and they are still rising on the average of 1/25th of an inch every year.

Such increases should not alarm anyone, unless, of course, man or nature generates some unforeseen catastrophic event. The steady rising of sea level has been caused by slow melting of the ice cap over the Antarctic and, to a lesser extent, glaciers in Greenland. If a gigantic heat wave or an atomic effect should melt all of Antarctica's 7 million cubic miles of ice, the world's seas would rise some 250 feet, and water would reach the nose level of the Statue of Liberty!

Lost Cities in the Sea

Polar areas are the chief sources of any additional water in the world, and their glaciers have melted and formed again periodically with temperature changes for a million years. With each glacial melting and reforming has come a corresponding rise and fall of the sea. About 19,000 years ago, according to Shepard, the seas were 300 to 400 feet below their present level. Earlier in prehistoric time they were even lower, possibly as low as 500 feet under the present level. At times, too, the seas have been higher than they are now, as much as 200 to 300 feet higher. The changes, most of which took place very slowly, explain the wide-spread submergence of building sites and other human relics along coastal areas. Actually, they did not submerge—the sea rose. Whole cities have been lost this way.

In Scandinavia, Labrador, and Newfoundland, land once held down by glaciers is now bobbing up like a slow-action cork, released by the melting of ice fields. Sometimes earthquakes push the land higher, masking a rise in sea level.

Recent Sea Risings

The Coast and Geodetic Survey, the oldest U.S. scientific agency, has done some pinpointing on the oceans which lap the shores of the United States. Since 1940 the sea has risen as much as 2 to 9 inches, the greatest increase being recorded at Eugene Island, Louisiana, 20 miles southwest of Morgan City, Louisiana. Along the Atlantic coast, a maximum rise of 5½ inches in the level of the sea was noted at Sandy Hook, New Jersey, while the record increase for the Pacific coast during the 1940-1964 period was 2 inches at San Diego, California, and Seattle, Washington.

According to the director of the Coast and Geodetic Survey (Rear Admiral H. Arnold Karo), these conclusions are based on data from 44 tide gauges operated along the coasts of the United States by the Department of Commerce agency. Data from these gauges are periodically analyzed for sea level trends. In all, the Coast and Geodetic Survey operates 106 tide gauges in the United States and its possessions. Accurate measurements show that rises in sea level since 1940 are different in different places. Baltimore, Maryland, shows an increase of 4 inches; New York, 3 inches; Boston, Massachusetts, and

Pensacola, Florida, 1½ inches; and San Francisco, California, only 1 inch. The tide gauge at Honolulu shows no appreciable overall change in the sea level there since 1940.

Also Land Sinking

Not all "apparent" rise in the sea should be attributed to a slightly warmer climate melting glaciers in polar areas. Land sinking has contributed significantly in various parts of the globe. For example, the "apparent" rise in the sea level at Galveston, Texas, has been 4½ inches since 1940, but the real rise has been something less because the land has settled there. In some areas the situation is reversed. The land is rising to such an extent at some places that the level of the sea is apparently sinking when actually it is rising.

What of the future—an anxious question for those who own low-level land, docks, small craft? Will the rising trends reverse themselves, or continue at the same rate? Coast and Geodetic Survey oceanographers say there is no indication that the rising trend will reverse itself and the sea level will start falling. However, they do note that the *rate of increase* has been diminishing somewhat during the last few years.

Changes in sea level have great economic ramifications in flat coastal areas. While an increase in the level of the ocean would have little effect on the steep shores of Maine, a similar rise in the Gulf of Mexico would cause the sea to encroach on thousands of acres of land. It would also cause havoc in surveying of reference marks, which, in turn, are often used as "taking off" points in establishing both offshore and land boundaries.

Lunar Drag May Slow Earth

Another theory, which may affect far off future generations, comes from the authoritative journal *Science*. This theory may also explain, in a measure, why the world has become gradually warmer and is showing an "apparent" rise in sea level. According to Dr. Gordon J. F. Macdonald, professor of geophysics at the University of California, Los Angeles, tidal friction exerted on the earth's surface by the moon is slowing the earth's rotation and causing the day to become longer. This in turn is slowly increasing the inclination of the earth's axis, which may result in an extension of present subtropical climate, such as that of Florida, into temperate zones and maybe further into polar regions.

Scientists point out that the tides raised in the plastic crust of the earth as well as in the oceans by the moon's gravity, are subject to certain frictional effects. By producing a torque, or twisting, in the crust, it acts as a brake to the earth's rotation.

At present, the earth rotates on its axis once in about 24 hours. Macdonald cites evidence that in the Middle Devonian Period of 350 million years ago, the day was only 21.7 hours long. According to studies of plant growth rates from fossil remains, the year had 400 days at that time instead of 365¼ days as it now has.

Beware of That Tilt!

Although it may not be noticeable in our time, the change in the earth's rate of rotation may increase the earth's tilt. The earth's axis is now inclined 23½ degrees to the plane in which the planet circles the sun—the plane of the ecliptic. Although this is the reason for seasons, Macdonald suggests this was not always so. In the far past, he believes, the inclination of the axis was much less than now. Consequently there was much less temperature variation between seasons and also between the poles and the equator.

To switch from the distant past to the present and the future, the question is, will the turbulent waters of the seas bring us more "living fossils" or perhaps a genuine "missing link" between mankind and the kingdom of marine animals? It would be a rash and indurate person who would say no, with so much of the depths still to be explored.

"Only the Morons Get Caught in a Net!"

Do not expect, however, for rare sea animals to be found in nets (William Beebe once observed: "Only the morons get caught in a net!"), nor seek for too many clues by dredging the bottom, or by drilling for cores. All these endeavors will help, but in the final analysis man must be present, using his own eyes, his own ears, and his other senses, combining them with instruments derived especially for the environment of the sea and the depths.

This calls, too, for unique hulls, which until only recently have been designed and created from what were once dream vehicles, the fantasies of science fiction. Using robust metal-and-glass spheres and cleverly operating minisubs with grappling appliances, man will soon be able to delve into every cranny and corner of Neptune's domain. Barriers that once shut off the mysteries of the depths will soon be penetrated by devices which have advanced beyond the drawing boards and are being tested at sea. By the time this volume is printed, many of these new devices may be off already on thrilling voyages of discovery, disclosing strange living creatures and other scientific treasures of the immense marine dominions which reign over nearly three-quarters of the earth.

CHAPTER II

MAN AND THE SEA

OCEANOGRAPHY AS A SCIENCE, or as a congeries, if you will, meaning a combination of several sciences, is quite young. As far as the learned man is concerned, the basic elements of the marine sciences date back less than a hundred years. Only in the last twenty-five years has the term "oceanographer" become even moderately well known. The recent growth of oceanography has been triggered by defense needs, and by an increasing interest in modifying the weather. These have swept with them a host of related factors—animal, vegetable, and mineral resources of the sea—as technical aids to man's welfare.

Long before oceanography or the marine sciences were recognized as such, however, man was acquiring their fundamentals. This concept holds today. The true oceanographer must be an *explorer* before he can hope to add to the world's store as a scientist or even as a technician. Laboratory work ashore must come hard upon the heels of preliminary findings made at sea, whether they be specimens, notes, graphs, photographs, or other scientific observations. Thus this sea-land combination has carved out a realm of something of its own as far as man is concerned.

Discovery of Sea's Use

Discovery of the sea's usefulness was one of man's earliest achievements, next probably to the use of fire and a few primitive tools. Imagine an energetic and ambitious primitive man at the edge of the sea, wanting to cross a bay or an estuary, or trying to reach a nearby island. He finds, by pushing a log ahead of him with his hands or legs, that he has an easier means of traveling—the first oceanic device for "conquering the sea." Logs tied together to make a raft became the next logical step; or maybe a dugout to keep him dry while afloat. Soon thereafter he developed paddles, oars, sails, and finally engines to abet or to overcome, as desired, the winds, currents, and waves, which assist man in using the sea.

Another early discovery: seawater is not drinkable by man. Yet from the ocean came food and also salt used as a preservative of fish and meat. Man learned that seawater could be evaporated by the sun to make various salts, and that by boiling seawater he could condense the steam into fresh water.

Eventually man developed ships, planes, and submarines to use to his advantage on the sea's surface, the air above the sea, and even portions of the depths below. It is thus that the mariner has overcome, after a fashion, the obstacles that have confronted him in oceanic research. Unlike a man on shore, who can do much of his scientific work alone, a researcher at sea is a helpless creature without the use of some kind of sizeable craft, or a sturdy pier, or a tower from an oil or other rig. Because the sea is so enormous, man cannot unlock its secrets without the aid of vessels, instruments, special equipment, food and fuel, and a host of other accessories.

Why So Far Behind?

Why has oceanography or marine research lagged so far behind other scientific pursuits? The answer, as indicated, lies in the very formidable obstacles involved in exploring an immense area or environment hostile to man. Not only does the sea not reveal even its surface and shallows readily to man, but it is even more stubborn about its alien depths. Cost is a major factor in hampering purely research expeditions as compared with voyages searching for gold and other treasures or in acquiring territory or trade.

Most needed, and still lacking, is men. Not just the rough and rugged seamen, who opened the oceans of the world, but *dedicated youngsters*. Once oceanographers were a lot like sailors; in fact, they were described as "sailors who use big words." But more than "big words" are needed to develop today's techniques of the sea, as sample by sample, sea mile by sea mile, fact by fact, the modern oceanographer assembles the work of special ships that will give us the secrets we must have in a highly competitive civilization.

Alexander As a Diver

At first man learned of oceanographic wisdom from scattered bits and fragments. A French manuscript of the 13th century presents Alexander the Great as a diver. The celebrated ruler, who sighed for new worlds to conquer, was, according to legend, the first man to go down into the sea merely to observe fish. Several later versions of the story declare that he saw a monster which took three days to swim past his glass cage!

In fact, much that we hear about the early days of the sea and its wonders must be *discounted* today—particularly "monsters" derived from old yarns spun in the forecastles of small sailing ships, or at little inns along the waterfront. These tales eventually were transferred into vivid print. Some of the sea monsters were purely imaginary, the result of one seaman trying to outdo a fellow narrator; others can be recognized as existing sea creatures, grotesquely distorted.

According to Dr. F. G. Walton Smith (*Sea Frontiers*, May 1961):

> Early chroniclers of natural history were not too careful about their sources of information and were, in fact,

rather apt to describe as first hand knowledge and even to provide detailed illustrations of sea monsters which were obviously based upon the over enthusiastic tales of fishermen and travellers. They also copied the works of earlier authors, often without giving due credit and in doing so incorporated further mistakes and exaggerations.

Maps Were Strategic Weapons

But much fairly accurate knowledge of the sea was also carried on by word of mouth from early ship captains and navigators. This hydrographic wisdom finally became so vast and complex that charts and other data on sheepskin were developed—the earliest "top secret documents"—to preserve monopolies of trade, or to withold information about newly discovered regions which might have as yet undeveloped riches. Maps became strategic weapons in the age of discovery and early empire building. Spanish sea captains were ordered to destroy their charts if threatened with capture; bootleg map making was likely to lead to prison or the torture chamber.

Unquestionably the earliest most noted mariner, one who considered oceanography by and for navigators, was Dom Henrique of Portugal. As Prince Henry the Navigator he set up a navigation data center in Sagres, at the southwestern corner of Portugal. This oceanic pioneer colonized the Madeiras, discovered the Azores and Cape Verdes, and had commenced the exploration of Africa's west coast when he died in 1460. His collection of charts or portolanos, books for navigators, were the finest of the times, but they were locked up after his death and held in the hands of a few for commercial enterprises.

Columbus Not Just Guessing

When Christopher Columbus told the King and Queen of Spain that the "Indies" could be reached through a shortcut by sailing west instead of east, he was not just guessing. For many years prior to his great voyage Columbus had made a living as a chart maker in Lisbon, then like Sagres, one of the great European centers of oceanic information of all kinds. While he found the wrong "Indies," Columbus's theories were correct in essence—he proved the world was *not* flat! His son Ferdinand later reported that his father had made a voyage to Iceland in February 1477, noting that the seas were not frozen in that season—perhaps the first hint of the Gulf Stream!

Although the Mediterranean gave birth to many sciences, the arts, and much of the classical world, this almost tideless basin offered little challenge to roving seafarers. So we must turn away from Mare Nostrum to greater events in exploration and discoveries elsewhere, some of which would lead the way to the marine sciences.

Not long after the death of Columbus, Ponce de Leon discovered, in his quest for the Fountain of Youth, that fabulous current known as the Gulf Stream. He knew that the Stream was something special, long before scientists found that it is the fastest current in the open sea—in places its speed is almost 11 miles per hour. Cruising near a cape later known as Kennedy, on a spring day in 1513, Ponce de Leon was startled to find his ships suddenly going backward in full sail instead of forward. Soon, Spanish mariners learned to avoid or follow the Stream to their advantage.

Franklin's First Chart

But not much scientific attention was paid to the Gulf Stream for nearly 200 years, until Nantucket whalers began to hunt sperm whales in 1712. It was not long before these canny seafarers recognized the advantage of keeping within the Stream when they sailed to England and the Continent, and in avoiding it on the western trip. At first they kept the secret to themselves. When Benjamin Franklin became postmaster of the northern colonies in 1753, he learned about this first oceanic "shuttle" during a visit to Nantucket, where his mother lived.

Anxious to speed the mail packets between England and the colonies, he mentioned the matter to the British Admiralty. But the stubborn sea captains of His Majesty's fleets wouldn't admit any upstart navigation notions from colonials, so the idea lay dormant. Finally, Franklin published it in 1783 as the first description of the Gulf Stream, which he called the North Atlantic Current.

For countless years storms and hurricanes have ravaged

the eastern coast of America and the West Indies. Man wondered about currents, waves, and winds that altered his life, but the study and treatment of the oceans did not interest him except as objects of curiosity. If the sea did not produce treasure, fish, or other commodities, or lead to territorial expansion, most people simply were not interested.

A first gleam of scientific attention, outside the dusty cabinets containing mineral and biological specimens in a few museums, came from an experiment made on board the U.S. frigate *President,* enroute to Tripoli. William Eaton listed in his journal, August 20, 1804, that while becalmed off Cabo de Gata, he "sunk a queen'sware plate over the stern, suspended on a log line, which was seen at a depth of 148 feet." This use of a depth marker was a rare occurrence because as yet there were no means of determining depths by mechanical devices.

Then Came Maury!

Like an eventual answer to an oceanographer's prayer arose Lieutenant Matthew Fontaine Maury, USN, who in 1842 undertook the first systematic study of the oceans as a full-time occupation. Maury, a brilliant and energetic young naval officer who had been crippled ashore at the peak of his career, refused to remain an invalid. At his request, he was appointed to the Navy's Depot of Charts and Instruments. From this Washington office, the direct ancestor of both the U. S. Naval Observatory and the U. S. Naval Oceanographic Office, Maury began his celebrated compilations of charts of winds, currents, temperatures, and other oceanographic data, derived from old logs and other sea reports.

By sheer coincidence the publication of Maury's first chart, enabling mariners to shorten their voyages by taking advantage of the currents and winds appeared in 1848, the year that gold was discovered in California. Travelers by sea in the Gold Rush of '49, speeded by his work, gave Maury wide recognition. He was asked to explain his methods at an international conference at Brussels in 1853, which paved the way for the first international cooperation in meteorology and oceanography by setting up the International Hydrographic Bureau and the World Meteorological organization.

"Pathfinder of the Seas"

As the U.S. Navy's first great genius ashore and the Navy's most brilliant early scientist, Maury mastered the oceans so well from his desk that he became known, even to his begrudging academic rivals, as the "Pathfinder of the Seas." Maury originally operated a modest *data center* at the Navy Depot, because *science*, as such, had not yet begun to attract major industry or big government. With his staff, Maury constantly improved his charts by tabulating observations of winds and currents by geographic areas and seasons and then analyzing the results to delimit the most favorable routes for sailing vessels. His routes, laid down on pilot charts and described in thick volumes of sailing directions, were exchanged with ship observers who promised to return filled-in data forms, sent to them by Maury.

While the world was quick to understand and use Maury's charts and sailing directions, he eventually became best known for a book—*The Physical Geography of the Sea*, a general treatise on oceanography published in 1855. This brilliant work is a milestone in the development of the marine sciences, and, almost unheard of in his time, it was written so that the intelligent reader could understand it. Maury's chapter on the Gulf Stream in this remarkable volume contains some of the finest prose ever written by a scientist—although some of Maury's pet theories have been disputed by others.

A recent Maury biographer, Frances Leigh Williams, concludes: "Although research in later years proved some of his concepts wrong, he was a bold workman who believed the beginnings had to be made." Dr. C. Alphonso Smith, when head of the English Department of the U.S. Naval Academy, declared: "It [*The Physical Geography of the Sea*] was the first book to embrace the entire sea as its theme and thus to bring three-quarters of the world into the domain of recognized and intelligent principle." What a wonderful motion picture Maury's life would make!

Emergence of Science

Thoughtful men, at the opening of the 19th century, were finally realizing the need for some kind of coordinated effort in the sciences, including the marine sciences, although the term "oceanography" was not to come into use until more than a century later. A small group in the Congress was sympathetic, to a degree, but no one in the early 1800's knew where, how, or when science should be placed in the scheme of things, or who should separate or combine its skills with the right men. It may be difficult today to understand the slow emergence of science as an organized force—*who* should study the stars, the weather, the sea and hundreds of research specialties—but it was a big problem. Lacking endowed foundations or well-funded academic institutions, and ahead of the need for mechanical instrumentation or "hardware" that might attract private industry, science perforce had to turn to the government. The few thinking people who expressed themselves in this direction suggested that science should *not* be tucked away under such huge departments as State, Treasury, or Agriculture, or the military services. In the beginning, however, science units were largely under the major departments, with only a few units operating under independent agencies.

Actually, the first federal scientific organization in the United States was the Coast Survey, established as a bureau of the Treasury Department in 1807. It has since been transferred to the Commerce Department as the Coast and Geodetic Survey, but its mission, greatly augmented, still calls for it to complete "an accurate chart of every part of the coasts—within twenty leagues of any part of the shores of the United States."

Today as the nation's chief *civilian* oceanographic agency, the Survey's personnel includes scientists, engineers, and technicians in cartography, geodesy, geomagnetism, gravimetry, photogrammetry, and seismology. It produces and distributes more than 30 million aeronautical and nautical charts. The Survey also oversees the operation of a worldwide earthquake network of seismographs which, when completed, will include 125 stations in 63 countries. It operates the Pacific Seismic Sea Wave Warning System, a network of some 60 tide stations which alerts people along the Pacific Basin of the onslaught of destructive seismic waves.

"Sea Curiosity" Helps

Scientific curiosity—a great deal of it about the sea—appears to rank high among men of outstanding ability in the mid-19th century. Among them was Joseph Henry, who in 1846 became the first Secretary of the Smithsonian Institution and was instrumental in the formation of the American Association of Science in 1848. Other notables in the same era were Louis and Alexander Agassiz, father and son, who revolutionized the methods of early oceanographic research and invented important new pieces of apparatus. Also memorable was Spencer Fullerton Baird, a grandson of Benjamin Franklin, who became the second secretary of the Smithsonian. He was largely responsible for setting up the first federal conservation agency—the U.S. Commission of Fish and Fisheries—on the issue that fishes were being depleted along the New Jersey and New England coasts.

It was through these active and energetic scientists, with a boost from Senator Henry Wilson of Massachusetts, that a charter was obtained for a National Academy of Sciences on March 3, 1863, the last day of the lame-duck 37th Congress. Signed by President Abraham Lincoln, the charter stated that the Academy's mission was: "to investigate, examine, experiment, and report upon any subject of science or art . . . whenever called upon by any Department of the Government."

On September 22, 1964, 101 years later, an *ad hoc* committee of distinguished scientists and engineers was formed by the National Academy of Sciences to advise the Congress on certain national problems involving scientific research. It was the first time that the Academy had been asked to provide continuing advice to the Congress— the result of an agreement between the Academy and the House Committee of the Congress.

Ancestral Home of All

It is natural that the publication of Darwin's *Origin of Species* in 1859 was a major event in the history of oceanography. As John Lyman, in *Ocean Sciences* (U.S. Naval Institute, 1964) summarizes Darwin's breakthrough:

> Previously, study of the oceans had been concerned with surface phenomena, of interest to navigators, or the form and composition of their bottoms, of concern to the infant technology of submarine cables. Now, however, the relationships between fossils as progenitors and living forms as descendants were clear; the *Systema Naturae*, of Linnaeus, was not merely a handy key to identification but a recognition of the evolution of living forms from the simple to the more complicated; and the sea was the ancestral home of all.

Darwin's work, however, involved much other science, some of it allied to the sea, some of it far removed. What we may date as the "formal beginning of oceanography" was on December 30, 1872, when the H.M.S. *Challenger* made its first "station" (halt at sea where observations are recorded) after leaving Portsmouth on a cruise that was to last four years and circumnavigate the globe. At this point the latitude was 41° 57′ N, the longitude was 9° 42′ W, and the depth was 1,125 fathoms. According to Joel W. Hedgpeth (Pacific Marine Station, California): "Nothing very remarkable was discovered, as the dredge did not work quite right and came up half empty—but with enough ice cold bottom mud nevertheless to chill a bottle of champagne we drank to the success of the expedition!"

A New Kind of Cargo

Despite its slow start, the H.M.S. *Challenger* brought home a wonderful cargo. For instead of gold, spices, ivory, or tobacco, this military steam corvette with its guns and shot removed had its hold filled with water samples, bottom samples, biological materials (fish, mammals, plankton, corals), some alive but mostly preserved, and tons of notes of measured water temperatures and other data.

The scientists came home with logbooks containing descriptions, analysis, and sketches that finally filled fifty massive and beautifully illustrated volumes. The most worthy objective of publishing complete results on an expedition, years after the return of the ship, was inaugurated by the *Challenger Reports,* now a collector's item prized by libraries and oceanographic institutions all over the world.

It was about this time, too, that another aspect of oceanography began to emerge, both in Europe and in America. These were seaside laboratories, where fresh specimens could be examined and studied, and aquaria, where living forms could be kept. In later years aquaria became entertainment features, rivaling zoos in attracting the general public. Imported tropical fish and mammals such as seals and porpoises have added amusement features.

Naples and Penikese

The first seaside laboratory was opened in 1872 at Naples, Italy. A year later, Louis Agassiz, founder of the Museum of Comparative Zoology at Harvard in 1859, set up a small summer laboratory on Penikese Island, off Cape Cod. It was soon abandoned, but the nearby Marine Biological Laboratory of Woods Hole, founded in 1888, is a direct descendant. Three years earlier, however, the first of the permanent establishments that have made Woods Hole the largest oceanographic center in the world was constructed by the Woods Hole Fisheries Station. Known locally as "The Fisheries," the station later became the Bureau of Commercial Fisheries Biological Laboratory, now a part of the Bureau of the Interior. Its new aquarium attracts some 200,000 visitors to Woods Hole annually.

England founded its first seaside laboratory, known as the Marine Biological Association of the United Kingdom, at Plymouth in 1888. It operates a public aquarium as well as research functions. The first laboratory on the Pacific coast was the Hopkins Biological Station of Stanford University, established at Pacific Grove in 1892. The famous Marine Biological Association of San Diego, at La Jolla, was endowed by members of the Scripps family in 1905. It became part of the University of California in 1912 as the Scripps Institution for Biological Research. It was redesignated in 1925 as the Scripps Institution of Oceanography.

A Host of New Laboratories

Shortly afterward (1930) the famous Woods Hole Oceanographic Institution was born, and a host of marine laboratories followed about the same period or shortly later. Included among others were the Oceanographic Laboratories of the University of Washington (1930); the Bingham Oceanographic Foundation, at Yale (1930); the Tidal Institute (England) was combined with the Liverpool Observatory (1929); Lamont Geological Observatory, Columbia University (1949); University of Miami Marine Laboratory (1947); Marine Laboratory, Duke University (1938); Department of Oceanography, Texas A. and M. College (1949), and a score of others of equal standing, both in the United States and abroad.

Throughout the period between World Wars I and II, oceanography was slowly but surely coming of age, through laboratories ashore, research ships at sea, various governmental agencies, and private commercial firms. While the name "oceanography" had not yet come into general use, an ancient term "oceanology" was sometimes used. More often, the word "hydrography" covered the ground, but not too well, because it was sometimes confused with "hydraulics," a common engineering term. Those who included oceanography among the "Earth Sciences" (as it is today) confused those who did not understand that "Earth" with a capital "E" is not the same as "land." So the growing pains went on.

Beebe and Bigelow

Meanwhile, the development of the marine sciences in the United States was greatly stimulated between the World Wars by two individuals—William Beebe and Henry B. Bigelow. As noted by John Lyman, *Ocean Sciences* (1964), "The former was responsible, through exploring, writing and lecturing, for creating public awareness of the existence of a field of scientific endeavor called oceanography; the latter, working more quietly in committees, persuaded private foundations and state and federal governments to provide the financial and logistic support for expanded effort in the field."

The work of both men attracted much oceanic interest in the United States and abroad, especially as the needs for submarine and antisubmarine warfare revealed that much more knowledge of the depths is required. Beebe's celebrated bathysphere, while it was more of an engineering feat than a scientific effort, focused public attention on modern exploration of the deep sea, and has, in recent years, helped to sprout a number of nonmilitary minisubs dedicated to marine research studies. Some of these ingenious vessels have been underwritten by the military and have been operated under charter by institutions and other scientific groups as well as by the Navy itself. Others have been built by private capital, and will be operated by private ships or will be chartered for special jobs or for the military.

Living Within Neptune's Realm

Space does not permit this book to describe all of these odd and unusual vehicles, but suppose we list a few of the larger or more famous ones, omitting those designed primarily for sports or pleasure purposes—although some of these can be useful for salvaging or for commercial fishing observations in shallow waters. In essence, the new fleet of manned submersibles demonstrates that before man can fully utilize the ocean and its resources for his own benefit, he must learn *to live within* Neptune's realm. During the sessions of the Marine Technology Society (1964), Dr. Athelstan Spilhaus made the point that recent conquests of sea frontiers have been accomplished through actual occupation of the area *after it has been explored,* and that this is as true for the ocean today as it was for any of the land frontiers of yesteryear. In other words, man will conquer the oceans when he has occupied them, and he will occupy them only after he has explored them. This exploration is under way now, through both manned and unmanned devices, alone or in tandem.

Actually there are so many underseas vehicles in action or under construction or being tested that it is difficult to classify them—whether by size, depth limit, tonnage, crew, exploration devices, tethered or untethered. Although it may not be the earliest, the bathyscaph *Trieste I*, designed and constructed by the Swiss Piccards, may be considered the "granddad of the deepest." The *Trieste II*, using a new U.S. Navy hull and the original sphere that was on *Trieste I*, made the record depth into the sea in 1960—35,800 feet, in the Mariannas Trench of the Pacific. It proved that with a ballast tank (gasoline), to which was attached a sphere for the crew, man could operate freely in the depths, although his range of travel would be limited by the power provided by batteries.

Locating the U.S.S. Thresher

It was the *Trieste II,* further improved, that discovered and photographed the remains of the U.S.S. *Thresher,* which sank in 8,400 feet of water during a test run, 200 miles off Cape Cod, in April 1963. With its grappling device *Trieste II* brought small pieces of the submarine to the surface in 1963. During the summer of 1964 it obtained clear pictures of parts of the hull itself. *Trieste II*'s new structure also permits faster towing speeds (10 knots instead of 4) on the surface.

While speaking of bathyscaphs and the Piccards, mention might be made here of the *Archimedes,* one of the largest vehicles of this type. It was built for the French Navy in 1961 and recently was engaged in a joint French-American project called "Deepscan" in the Puerto Rico Trench (27,500 feet deep). Those taking part in this joint enterprise were the French Navy, the National Scientific Research Center of France, Lamont Geological Observatory (Columbia University), Woods Hole, and the U.S. Navy Electronics Laboratory.

A *mesocaph,* or mid-depth vehicle, has been built by Dr. Jacques Piccard, son of the Swiss scientist Auguste Piccard, for whom it is named. Operated for the Swiss Exposition at Lausanne, Switzerland, this 93.4-feet-long mesocaph might be termed a pleasure craft, with its 40 passengers and a crew of four making several quick dives a day. But its 3,000-foot descent (only 1,000 feet for tourists) and its speed (in excess of 6 knots) promise usefulness for science. In fact, funds for a duplicate are being sought.

The mesocaph *Auguste Piccard* is unique in that the compressibility of its hull is less than that of seawater. The advantage of this is that it can find a depth (density) of water, adjust to zero bouyancy, and hover there indefinitely with no further adjustments. One of the first missions of the proposed second craft, Dr. Piccard hopes, will be to drift at mid-depth in the Gulf Stream for a month or six weeks continually submerged. Its position would be kept at a safe level through both acoustic and special "long wave" navigation techniques.

Emergency Features

Although it is one of the medium-sized vehicles to join the armada of deep-sea devices, *Alvin* has several unique aspects, including safety features in case of an emergency. Designed specifically for oceanographic research, *Alvin* has a depth of 6,000 feet, is 22 feet long, is capable of a 6- to 8-knot top speed, and has a cruising speed of 2.5 knots for 20 to 25 miles submerged. To obtain buoyancy in case of emergency, all three batteries and the trim-system mercury can be dropped; or, if entangled in a derelict cable or chain, the big mechanical arm can be easily disconnected. As a last resort, its pressure sphere or cabin can be released and will surface in an upright position. A large catamaran lowers and raises the craft at the surface between dives or when batteries, air flasks, food, or repairs are needed. The barge will have sufficient deck space to mount three portable vans to handle such operations.

Alvin was funded by the Office of Naval Research and was built by the Applied Science Division of Litton Industries for the Woods Hole Oceanographic Institution, which will operate it at sea.

Most unusual of the larger deep-sea non-military vehicles is the controversial all-aluminum submersible *Aluminaut*, launched at the General Dynamics Electric Boat shipyard, September 1, 1964. Because the forged rings comprising its hull are bolted together rather than welded and for other reasons, the Navy and the Woods Hole Oceanographic Institution have declined its offered services, ordering *Alvin* instead. J. Louis Reynolds, Board Chairman of Reynolds International, Inc., is so convinced with *Aluminaut*'s possibilities that he spent $3 million to develop the world's first aluminum and deepest diving submarine (depth 15,000 feet) without any support from government funds. *Aluminaut* may prove to be a forerunner of a class of submersibles employing new fabrication techniques.

Subs Sprouting Everywhere

Because the submarine has emerged out of the highly restrictive and costly categories of military weapons platforms, scores of small undersea civilian devices are sprouting at scores of shipyards from coast to coast. Here are just a few—some in operation, others building, and others in active planning stages—as selected from *Undersea Technology* (August 1964): *Ashera*, General Dynamics Electric Boat, for the University of Pennsylvania Museum, to be used for marine archeology exploration; *Benthos V*, Lear-Siegler, can carry 400 pounds of special equipment; *Cub-marine PC-38*, Perry Submarine Builders for Weston, can carry 100 pounds, available for lease from Weston; *Deep Jeep*, U.S.N. Ordnance Test Station, China Lake; *Denise* or *Flying Saucer*, Captain J. Costeau (French), can carry 1,000 to 1,500 pounds of personnel and equipment; *Kuroshio*, Japanese Fisheries, requires single cable to surface for power; *Severyanka*, U.S.S.R., converted submarine used only for research; *Submaray*, Hydrotech Company, for charter or contract work; *Yomiuri*, Shin Mitsubishi Shipyard, Japan, research on fisheries; *Deep Star*, Westinghouse Electric Corporation, will have negative buoyancy when dive starts, ballast dropped to halt for level operations and to ascend; *Dolphin*, U.S.N. Portsmouth Navy Yard, experimental submarine, classified; *Beaver*, North American Aviation, Inc., Autonetics Div., hydraulic propulsion; *Turtle*, Lockheed Missile and Space Co., lens shaped hull, for salvage, rescue, and research.

Not submarines, but related to them in manned research in the depths, are bottom tanks and tents. These are used as submerged bases for salvage, exploration, and research by scuba divers. The *Sealab*, a pioneer U.S. Navy project, permitted four aquanauts to live and work for three weeks under water with no ill effects. Its capsule was moored 192 feet beneath the ocean surface at Artemis Argus Island, 26 miles southwest of Bermuda. The four aquanauts were lowered to the ocean bottom in a tiny submarine decompression chamber. Astronaut Scott Carpenter originally was scheduled to spend part of the test in the capsule during a side experiment, but he broke his arm in a Bermuda motorbike accident ashore!

Inflated Rubber Tent

An even deeper dive, using an inflated rubber tent, was carried out by a team conducted by inventor Edwin A. Link and sponsored by the National Geographic Society and the Smithsonian Institution. Two divers spent more than two days at an ocean depth of 430 feet near Great Stirrup Cay, a small isle in the Bahamas. Mr. Link, who designed the submersible, portable, inflatable dwelling, called it *Spid*. The group carried two other essential pieces of equipment: a submersible decompression chamber (SDC), and a larger, shipboard decompression chamber that was coupled to the SDC.

Mention of the Links, both Ed and his wife Marion, discloses another phase of modern oceanography—underwater archeology—of which they are among the first to explore scientifically. Mr. Link's entry into this fascinating world was, oddly enough, through aviation. As the designer of the first Link flight-trainer, later adopted by the U.S. armed forces and developed into today's complicated electronic flight simulators, he was concerned also with navigation and reliable instruments.

At the close of World War II he sought a change from the pressing demands of office work and took up sailing. Soon he was diving among ancient wrecks in the Florida Keys from his 43-foot yawl *Blue Heron*, and later from a converted shrimp boat that became the first *Sea Diver*. His present *Sea Diver* Mr. Link designed from the keel up as a diving research vessel. With it he operates also a bottom tent-dwelling, a compression-decompression chamber, atmosphere analyzers, and other equipment which is the result of his early diving experiences.

A New Field—Archeology

Since 1951, Mr. and Mrs. Link have devoted themselves to the need for more knowledge and better tools in underwater research. They have led archeological undersea expeditions to Caesarea and the Sea of Galilee, in Israel; to the sunken city of Port Royal, Jamaica; to Cap Haitien, Haiti; to the Bahamas; and to Syracuse, Sicily.

Tests with the Links' new *Spid*, or undersea chamber,

are aimed principally at longer visits on the sea bottom, whether for archeology, or ordinary salvage, or even fisheries studies. Under present methods, a scuba diver, after only one hour at 300 feet, must return to the surface and be decompressed for 7.36 tedious hours, to avoid the "bends." Thus the amount of useful work he can produce is severely limited. If the diver can remain or live underwater, however, he can work as long as it is necessary, and undergo decompression only once—at the end of his long, deep dive. This is the key to Mr. Link's "Man-in-Sea" project.

And Even Diamonds!

Working down as far as 600 feet, divers should be able soon to open up the untapped resources of the earth's continental shelves—an area of some 10 million square miles, almost the size of Africa. This bottom land is rich with minerals, fuel, food, and even diamonds! Yet, as Mr. Link says, "Man remains, in this realm, on a par with the aborigines. We are simple *hunters* of the sea, rather than *farmers*. Our best estimate is that some 490 billion pounds of fish could be harvested each year without harming the 'flocks'. This is five times the world's present catch."

No wonder then that Mr. Link feels, as he wrote in the June 1964 issue of the *National Geographic,* that "the great age of discovery certainly did not end with Columbus, Magellan, or Cook. It may well lie in the future."

Another unusual research vessel now undergoing tests is Aerojet-General's SPAR (for Seagoing Platform for Acoustic Research). Like the earlier ship FLIP (Floating Instrument Platform), this odd vessel is taken to sea in a horizontal position, and then is tilted to the vertical. While SPAR will be unmanned, it will be operated with two nearby AGOR (Auxiliary General Oceanographic Research) vessels. One will tow it out to its operational area and erect it into the vertical position. The research vessel will be connected to SPAR by means of a 3,000-foot-long floating power and data transmission cable. The other ship will act simply as a target, generating sounds of various types from various depths—such as above and below the thermocline.

Of Interest to the Navy

The primary purpose of SPAR, which is 354 feet long and 16 feet in diameter, is the study of submarine passive listening phenomena and detection ranges under all oceanic conditions. Of special interest to the Navy are the acoustics encountered along vertical oceanic interfaces, such as the temperature discontinuities along the Gulf Stream and other major oceanic currents. After outfitting in 1965, SPAR and its two AGOR's will proceed to AUTEC (Atlantic Underwater Test and Evaluation Center), in the Tongue of the Oceans, the Bahamas, for calibration. After that they will operate from a base at Solomons, Virginia, and conduct research off the Virginia and North Carolina Capes—much of it in the close vicinity of the Gulf Stream.

Massive Assault on Indian Ocean

Until recent years, oceanography was carried out at sea with single ships, or perhaps with only one or two in conjunction. This leaves important gaps and sometimes means overlap. Now whole fleets of ships have been coordinated on a single project, extended over several months or years. Take, for instance, the International Indian Ocean Expedition (IIOE), which was proposed in the summer of 1960 as a many-sided international attack on problems relating to a better understanding of the "vast environmental laboratory" of the Indian Ocean. A boost came from the United States, through a prospectus from the White House on June 13, 1960, calling for a series of scientific cruises and pledging U.S. contributions to this multi-nation effort.

By 1962 oceanographers from 28 nations were probing the mysteries of the world's third largest ocean. More than 40 ships were taking innumerable measurements and samples from the west coast of Australia to the Bay of Bengal, from the Arabian Sea to eastern Africa. IIOE will continue through 1965.

Sources of U.S. Support

Principal support for U.S. research ships and scientific programs has been provided by the Navy and by the

MAN AND THE SEA • 53

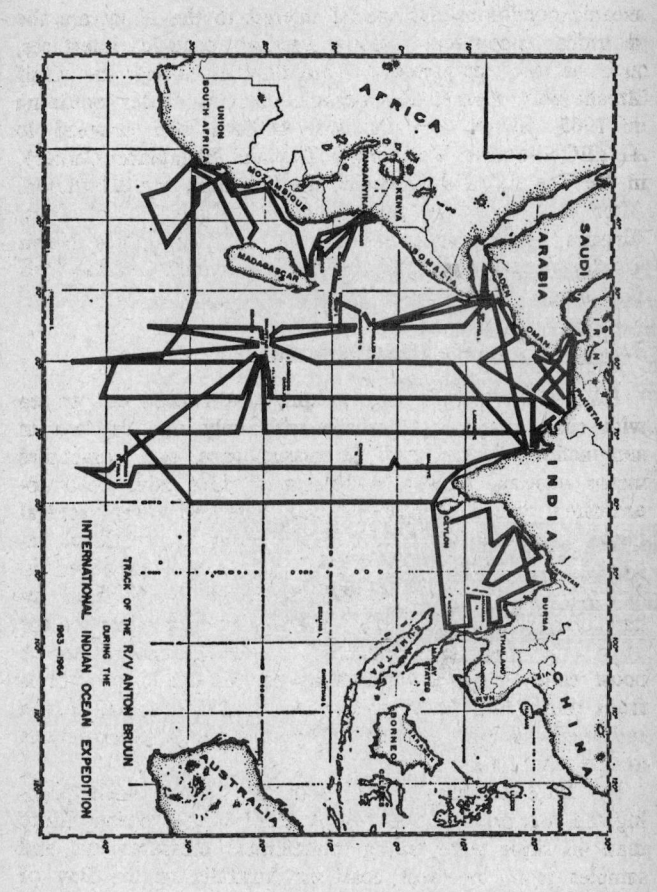

TRACK OF
THE R/V ANTON BRUUN
DURING THE
INTERNATIONAL INDIAN OCEAN
EXPEDITION
1963—1964

(National Science Foundation)

National Science Foundation. To a lesser but important degree, U.S. programs have also received support from the Weather Bureau, Bureau of Commercial Fisheries, the Coast and Geodetic Survey, and the Smithsonian Institution.

According to Smithsonian's Dr. I. E. Wallen, writing in the *I.G. Bulletin*, (National Academy of Sciences),

> "U.S. plans and programs are loosely coordinated with those of other countries in order to provide for an optimum balance of research in scientific programs and for cooperating scheduling of observations. These cooperative endeavors should yield a large body of comparable data that will assist in explaining large-scale phenomena related to the Indian Ocean Fisheries and to the seasonally reversed monsoon winds.
>
> "Results thus far from IIOE include masses of data in the World Data Centers in Moscow and in Washington, as well as in the Meteorological Center in Bombay. Specimens have been deposited in the Indian Ocean Biological Center (Cochin), in the Smithsonian Oceanographic Sorting Center (Navy Yard, Washington), and in research laboratories of various countries."

Not directly related to IIOE's program, but carrying out scientific missions in the Indian Ocean area, is the U.S.A.F. tracking ship *General Hoyt S. Vandenberg*, capable of gathering 20 million bits of information on a launched missile. It carries some of the most complex and sophisticated electronic equipment ever taken to sea.

A Synoptic Survey

Another cooperative oceanic group organized during 1963 and 1964 was the—take a deep breath—International Cooperative Investigations of the Tropical Atlantic (ICITA). Ships from seven countries, including the United States, converged on the Atlantic in an area stretching from South America to Africa. During two-week periods each of eleven ships made the same measurements along a series of north-south lines across the Equator. Thus scientists were able to get for the first time an almost photographic picture of a large section of the ocean—a synoptic survey.

According to Dr. Harris B. Stewart, Jr., chief oceanographer, U.S. Coast and Geodetic Survey,

"The problem in the past has been that the things you are trying to measure—water temperature, currents, salinity, dissolved oxygen concentration, animal abundances, and the like—all vary so rapidly with *time* that it is difficult to make sense from the observations made by a single ship covering a large area over a long period of time."

Yet despite the obvious need for more coordinated international effort, the necessity has not passed for an important oceanographic ship operating *alone* over large sea areas, as did the redoubtable H.M.S. *Challenger*. So take note today of U.S.N.S. *Eltanin,* a new floating research laboratory maintained by the National Science Foundation. Since 1962, without any escort, *Eltanin* has been making difficult but extremely valuable studies in the storm-tossed waters that envelop Antarctica, the loneliest part of the sea. Its rugged six-week cruises are interrupted only briefly by halts to resupply at Valparaiso, Chile, or some other southern port.

Eltanin, with a length of 266 feet and full load displacement of 3,886 tons, accommodates about 32 scientists and technicians (occasionally including women scientists) and is operated by a 47-man civilian crew of the U.S. Navy's Military Sea Transportation Service. The ship has been equipped not only for physical oceanography and marine biology studies but also for atmospheric physics research, submarine geology, and meteorology. It enables U.S. scientists to do research in areas of the world that have scarcely been explored, let alone studied scientifically.

CHAPTER III

CURRENTS, WAVES, AND THE LIKE

WHILE NOT VERY GLAMOROUS, the physical properties of the sea are significant and are not too uninteresting. Contrary to popular belief and to obvious appearance, the oceans of the world are not static bodies, but great moving masses of water. The normal rotation of the earth, the gravity pull of moon and sun, the movement of the wind and storms, and temperature changes and chemical variations combine to disturb and highly stratify layers of the ocean. Near the Poles, cold water sinks and moves sluggishly toward the Equator. On the surface, more rapid currents thread their way through great "rivers in the sea," such as the Gulf Stream, El Niño, and the Humboldt and Japan currents.

Near shore, the patterns of the waves and coastal currents are constantly changing. Tides lift huge masses of water onto the shoreline, then pull them back again. Powerful and submerged movements, such as the Cromwell Current in the Pacific, wind through the depths. Understanding of these short- and long-term variations in circulation is a prime key to oceanography.

However much we may know about sea movements, though, much study, ingenuity, and patience are still required, and answers will come slowly as the gear and techniques are refined bit by bit, sometimes haphazardly. Detailed observations at sea should be augmented by theory, that is, with mathematical and physical analysis applied to problems of fluids in motion, and by checking the resulting hypothesis again in the laboratory or at sea. All of which takes time and explains why many oceanographic answers will not be found overnight, even with the latest computers and electronic devices.

"Operation Cabot"

Most of the principal surface currents of the world oceans were discovered during the great age of sea exploration, in the late 15th and during the 16th centuries. It was not until the 1800's that close examination of the deepwater circulation began, and not until within the last decade or two that several major undersea features were disclosed, such as the great undercurrents, and close examination was made of the mid-Atlantic and other submarine ridges and mountain ranges.

Recent research shows that the Gulf Stream becomes even more complicated as it is examined by modern oceanographers. In 1950, during "Operation Cabot," a multiship study of the Stream took place east of Cape Hatteras. Woods Hole Oceanographic Institution oceanographers came up with a series of currents, sometimes disconnected and overlapping like shingles on a roof. Occasionally large meanders developed; some broke off into circular eddies hundreds of miles in diameter.

"Now even the CABOT picture appears to have been oversimplified," report WHOI scientists, as data from a more intensive 10-week survey in 1960 are beginning to demonstrate.

> "In Operation GULF STREAM 60, several ships, *RV Chain*, *RV Atlantis* and *RV Crawford*, and the International Ice Patrol cutter *Evergreen*, ran eleven parallel north-south lines of hydrographic stations about 100 miles apart from the continental shelf to the latitude of Bermuda. Additional observations were made of the currents both on the surface and in the deep water. The results indicate that the meanders are more stable and go deeper than had been thought, and that the Stream itself appears to run deeper than the one-mile maximum previously calculated. At the same time a new study of meanders southwest of Hatteras indicates that, instead of dissipating the energy of the Stream, as had been believed, they actually contribute to it."

Gulf Stream, an Enigma

In any event, we may now discard the romantic conception of the Gulf Stream as simply a warm, blue, swift-running ocean river that saves Iceland, the British Isles, and northern Europe from turning into a setting for polar bears. To oceanographers, the Stream still has so many little-known aspects that the best definition for it is "an enigma." Serious study of the Stream began in 1844. Recent research, carried out with modern scientific tools, suggests that it contains more areas and activities than were suspected. One recent expedition discovered, for instance, that off Florida the Stream seems to have a pulse which makes the water flow in repeated thrusts like blood in an artery.

Many oceanographers no longer think of the Gulf Stream as just a great river snaking across the North Atlantic. They regard it, rather, as a barrier separating cold Arctic waters from the warm Sargasso Sea.

"The intensity of flow of the Stream, the Stream's direction, and its temperature are not primary climatic factors in determining the climate of Europe," writes Henry Stommel, of Woods Hole Oceanographic Institution, in his comprehensive book *The Gulf Stream*. "But the role which it plays in determining the northern boundaries and average temperature structure of the Sargasso Sea must be of critical importance."

In simpler terms, the nearby Sargasso acts also as a huge hot-water tank for Europe, although dispersal of its comforting warmth is controlled, to a large extent, by the pace of the Gulf Stream. Paradoxically, Europe would become colder, not hotter, if the Gulf Stream should begin to flow faster. The effect would be not to carry more warmth, but to tighten the barrier about the Sargasso.

A Desert-Like Sea

Actually, the currents of the entire Gulf Stream system sweep in a gigantic elliptical orbit about the western North Atlantic and enclose the Sargasso, which suggests a vast ocean desert, with little marine life. It extends more than halfway across the Atlantic; Bermuda is an off-center pivot on the Sargasso's east-west axis.

The Gulf Stream itself begins its journey in the narrow cleft between Florida and the Bahamas. It gushes northward through the Florida Straits at a rate of about a hundred billion tons of water an hour, taking a surprisingly narrow course up the open Atlantic past Newfoundland. Here the Stream breaks into a series of branches known as the North Atlantic Current. One branch curves back under Iceland, ultimately to help flush icebergs from Davis Strait. Some branches shoot off past Scandinavia; others turn south to Spain and Africa, with enough momentum swinging back west to the West Indies and Caribbean Sea to aid in launching the Stream anew.

Speediest Open-Sea Current

The speediest current ever found in the open sea—almost 11 miles an hour—was measured off Florida in the Gulf Stream. In contrast, a normal oceanic current lazes along at a pace of a half to one mile an hour, and as a rule the Gulf Stream seldom exceeds 4 to 5 miles an hour.

In time, oceanographers learned that the Gulf Stream is misnamed. Some of the currents feeding the Stream surge through the Gulf of Mexico, but they mix hardly at all with Gulf waters. Other currents move northward along the east side of the Bahamas before they join the main Stream off the Carolinas.

Close study of any fast-moving, fluctuating river in the open sea will remain difficult. But new ideas and instruments continue to examine the Gulf Stream through expert organizations, such as the Coast and Geodetic Survey, Woods Hole, the Navy Oceanographic (formerly Hydrographic) Office, the Coast Guard, the University of Miami's Marine Science, the National Geographic Society, and others.

Periodic Motion of Waves

Beyond specific currents on and in the sea, what causes the periodic motion of the waters of the globe? The short answer is: attractive forces of various celestial bodies, principally the moon and sun, upon different parts of the rotating earth. Such forces can be either a help or a hindrance to the mariner—the water's rise and fall may at certain times provide enough depth to clear a bar and at others may prevent him from entering or leaving a harbor. At sea, the flow of current may help his progress or hinder it, may carry him toward dangers or away from them. Fortunately, the mariner making intelligent use of

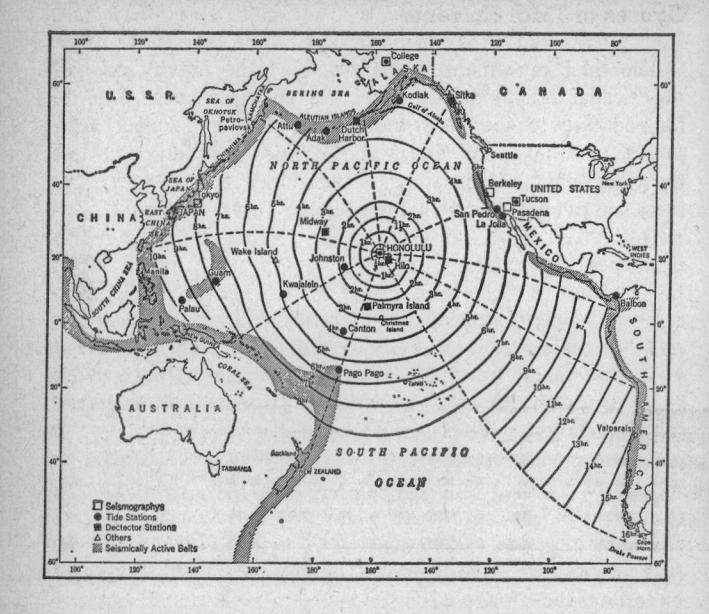

Seismic Seawave Travel-Time Chart
(U.S. Coast and Geodetic Survey)

predictions published in tide and tidal current tables, plus descriptions in sailing directions, can set his course to make the tide serve him, or at least to avoid its dangers or delays.

In its rise and fall, the *tide* is accompanied by a periodic horizontal movement of the water called *tidal current*. The two movements, tide and tidal current, are intimately related, forming parts of the same phenomenon brought about principally by the tide-producing forces of the sun and the moon.

However, let us distinguish clearly between tide and tidal current, for the relation between them is not a single one, nor is it everywhere the same. To avoid misunderstanding, the mariner should adopt the technical usage: *tide* for the vertical rise and fall of the water, and *current* for the horizontal flow. The tide rises and falls; the tidal current floods and ebbs. (In British usage, tidal current is called *tidal stream*).

Causes of Tidal Currents

The tidal movement is the result of the gravity or pull of celestial bodies acting upon the rotating earth. Due to its nearness to the earth, the moon is the stronger tide-producing body. The effect of the sun is reduced to less than half that of the much smaller moon. Other celestial bodies can be discounted because their pull is almost non-existent. The actual tide-producing force results from the difference in the attraction of either the moon or sun upon the various particles that make up the earth, the differences being due to the unequal distances between the particles and the center of the tide-producing body.

For example, as the moon travels around the earth it exerts its maximum pull on the particles nearest to it; less on one at the earth's center, and its smallest pull on one farthest away on the other side.

If the surface of the earth were covered entirely with water capable of responding instantly to the pull of the moon, the surface would consist of two high-water bulges, one on the side closest to the moon and the other on the opposite side of the earth, with a low-water belt around the earth between them. But due to the irregular distribution of land and water over the earth's surface, and the effects of friction and inertia, the actual effect of the force is to produce a very complicated system of oscillations or variations in the ocean basins. The earth rotating on its axis causes an apparent movement of the high-water bulges in a westerly direction, which accounts for the progression of the tides and currents.

Two Major Types of Currents

Oceanographers in their attempts to unravel the factors that bring about currents, in order to understand their nature and thus predict their changes, have found that currents fall into two large classes: tidal currents and non-tidal currents.

The horizontal tidal currents, like the vertical movement of the tides, are periodic, passing through regular cycles of flood and ebb. The current which floods and ebbs through the approaches to Boston Harbor is an example of a tidal current. Non-tidal currents are not necessarily periodic and they often flow in the same general direction all year. The Gulf Stream, for instance, is this type of current—brought about by winds, temperature difference of seawater in different areas of the oceans, and other factors.

For this discussion, let us deal with the ordinary tidal current having a period of about 12½ hours (the type along the Atlantic coast of the United States). Studies of current observations have revealed that tidal currents may be either reversing or rotary:

(1) *Reversing current.* In any restricted area, such as a bay or tidal river, the current is primarily the reversed type; that is, the flood current runs in one direction for about 6 hours and the ebb current for a similar time in the opposite direction. During each change of direction a period of slack water occurs. The velocity increases continuously from slack water up to the strength of either ebb or flood. The velocity of current as well as the range of tide varies from day to day during the month, according to the phase, distance, and declination of the moon. For example, the velocity of strength of current through the Golden Gate, at San Francisco, varies from about 1 knot to as much as 6 knots.

(2) *Rotary currents.* Rotary currents are generally found off-shore, continuously changing direction and having no slack water period. This change in directions may be clockwise or counterclockwise for different locations. In a period of about 12½ hours a rotary current may flow in all directions of the compass and the velocity vary in a regular manner from hour to hour. The minimum and maximum velocities of the rotary current are related to each other in the same manner as slack and strength of reversing current. A minimum velocity of current follows a maximum velocity by an interval of about 3 hours, and is in turn followed by another maximum after a further interval of about 3 hours.

The Coast and Geodetic Survey has made current observations in many harbors, bays, and rivers and at lightships anchored in open water. The simplest form of apparatus for observing currents consists of the current pole and log line. The velocity is determined by the amount of line paid out in one minute of time. The direction of the current, as indicated by the position of the pole, is determined by compass or sextant.

Using Anchored Buoys

During hydrographic surveys, current buoys are anchored at selected locations throughout the area to be surveyed. Beneath each of these buoys, current meters are suspended at predetermined depths to measure the direction and velocity of currents at these depths. Stabilizing fins on the meter keep the instrument headed into the current, while the impeller turns at a rate reflecting the speed of the water. This information is transmitted in the form of coded radio signals to the ship, where it is recorded on tape. The current meter used for this type of work is capable of measuring velocities as low as 1/10 knot.

Tidal Current Tables, issued annually in advance by the Coast and Geodetic Survey, give daily predictions of the times of slack water and the times and velocities of the flood and ebb current for many places along the Atlantic and Pacific Coasts. Supplemental data is included by which tidal current predictions can be determined for about 1,900 places, in addition to those for which daily predictions are given.

Another means of providing available current data to the mariner and the hydrographic engineer is a series of *Tidal Current Charts* for various harbors. These charts depict the direction and velocity of the tidal current for each hour of the tidal cycle. When used with the proper current tables or tide tables, the 12 charts, printed in color and bound into a single booklet, portray for each tidal hour the current that may be expected throughout the entire reaches of a given harbor.

Deep Counter Currents

One of the more fascinating aspects of oceanography is that no matter how up-to-date you become, periodically up comes something entirely new that tips the boat and requires not only adjustments but sometimes needs complete revision. This happened in 1952 when Townsend Cromwell, of the U.S. Fish and Wildlife Service, discovered sea undercurrents that move far below the surface on courses of their own.

Cromwell, studying methods of tuna fishing in the Pacific, found that long lines set at the Equator did not drift *west* with the Equatorial Current, as expected, but moved rapidly *eastward*. Further investigation revealed that the deep Cromwell Current is about 250 miles wide, and runs east along the Equator a distance of at least 3,500 miles. Equally startling, another current was indicated underneath the Cromwell, flowing *westward*!

Ever since the discovery of the Cromwell Current, scientists assumed that similar counter currents would be found in the Atlantic. Sure enough, counter currents have shown up there and in various other areas, including the Indian Ocean.

The first analyzed data from this Atlantic undercurrent was found while scientists from Columbia University and the Department of Interior's Fish and Wildlife Service were studying the fishery potential in the Gulf of Guinea, aboard the Bureau of Commercial Fisheries' oceanographic vessel *Geronimo*. Thomas L. Austin, director of the Bureau's Biological Laboratory, said the primary purpose of the survey was to obtain new information about fisheries along the west African coast, during which the Guinea undercurrent was examined.

Actually presence of the South Atlantic undercurrent was first indicated in the summer of 1962, during a previous voyage of the *Geronimo*. Equipment lowered into the easterly flowing Guinea current was suddenly pulled to the west. A current meter used during the latest voyage indicated the continued presence of the undercurrent, but since both observations were made in similar weather conditions, the scientists now want to study it during another season to determine its permanence. This will be done during the *Geronimo's* next trip to the Gulf of Guinea.

Open Ocean Tide Network

Until recently, the Coast and Geodetic Survey has restricted its studies in tides to the coasts of the United States or to parts of the world where no foreign islands did the work. The Coast and Geodetic Survey has now inaugurated an open ocean tide program, with successful completion of two series of observations on the Atlantic continental shelf, well beyond the 3-mile limits of the United States.

The measurements were made with two bottom-mounted

gauges; one in 840 feet of water, located 73 miles south of Block Island, the other in 690 feet of water, 93 miles southeast of Nantucket. A mean range of 3.5 feet was measured at the former location, while 2.8 feet was measured at the latter. Thus was launched a new and continuing program of the Geodetic Survey in establishing an open ocean tide network throughout the world oceans. Emphasis will be placed on the Atlantic continental shelf and selected guyots (flat-topped underseas mountains) far from continents and islands.

The main instrument used comprises a pressure transducer, whose signal is amplified by a direct current amplifier, then fed into a strip chart recorder. Although tide observations in the open ocean (free of islands and structures) are not new, they are rare. The Coast Survey feels it has probably developed the first truly operational instrument. Designed by Mr. Marc Goodheart, of the Survey's instrument division, it is accurate to the nearest tenth of a foot well beyond 1,000 feet, although the extreme limit is still unknown.

Coriolis and Ekman

One usual term that comes up now and then in reference to sea currents is "the Coriolis force." Its effect is to cause a moving object (seawater) to be deflected because of the earth's rotation. In the Northern Hemisphere it deflects water to the right; in the Southern Hemisphere, to the left. This force has shown to have considerable influence on major water currents.

According to Bretschneider and Mehaute, *Ocean Sciences*, 1964:

> "It is under the action of the gradient of the relative slope of the free surface, the shearing stresses caused by wind action and bottom friction, the variations of specific gravity, and the Coriolis forces that a complex flow pattern of currents takes place in the ocean.
>
> "However, some laws can be demonstrated in idealized cases. Because of the Coriolis force and the friction force, the current velocity has a tendency to decrease with depth and to change in direction. This phenomenon is called Ekman's spiral. It also explains why icebergs travel on the right of the wind direction."

Wind Waves, the Commonest

Of all the many things we know about the sea, wind waves are the most common. Some of them are set up by the immediate wind, some are from disturbances generated far away. Swells observed in England, for instance, have traveled from storms as distant as the South Atlantic. While waves can be dangerous to ships, most large vessels go on their courses by slowing the engines a bit. Most waves in the open sea are not more than 12 feet high; waves from 25 to 50 feet in height are rare. The record to date is a wave estimated 112 feet high, noted in 1933 by the U.S. Navy tanker *Ramapo*, enroute from the Philippines to San Diego.

Most oceanographers and navigators, however, are more concerned with waves as they affect the shore. To understand what actually goes on there, one must know the terms oceanographers use to describe waves.

Harris B. Stewart, Jr., chief oceanographer U.S. Coast and Geodetic Survey, has summarized these terms in *The Global Sea* (1964). In brief they are: (1) *Wave length*. Horzontal distance from one crest to the next. (2) *Height of a wave*. The vertical distance between the bottom of a trough and the crest of the next wave. (3) *Period*. The time between the passage of one crest and the passage of the next one at a given point. (4) *Wave velocity*. The speed of advance of the wave crest. Thus any simple regular train of waves can be described in these four terms.

Whitecaps Come into Play

In essence, typical waves are formed by the action of wind on water—the area where the sea surface and the enveloping mantle of air are in intimate contact with the consequences of weather and climate. As winds blow over the sea, they push its rippling surface into ridges and furrows. As the *ridges* or wave forms begin to move shoreward, they continue to grow. If the wind sharply increases, foaming *whitecaps* form along the crest of the wave, creating the typical appearance of the *sea in a storm*. Waves in a storm region form an extremely irregular pattern, seemingly moving in complete disorder and confusion. This is what is known as a *sea*. In its course shoreward, however, waves may iron out a bit, becoming evenly spaced undulations called *swells*.

Often the full fury of a sea hits the coast head-on, particularly if the shoreline lies in the path of waves that have been driven over unobstructed water by constantly heavy winds. Islands that lie off the west coast of Scotland, for instance, are famous for unsurpassed power of *surf*, the chief geologic agent in sculpturing the coasts of the world. The Pacific coast, from northern California to the Canadian border, also receives the force of storm surf generated thousands of miles away. Such waves can move rocks that wreck lighthouses and other shore structures weighing thousands of tons.

Strange Unseen Waves

Some of the largest and most powerful waves are never seen, nor are likely to be observed by ordinary man. They occur in depths of almost 4 miles below the surface, and may range as high as 100 feet! Oceanographers of Columbia University's Hudson Laboratories recently disclosed this hidden turbulence by using special aluminum spheres, which can float under water at any desired depth down to 20,000 feet. These submarine satellites relay information back with sonic pings resembling cricket chirps.

According to Alan Berman, director of the project, the first experiments in the Caribbean Sea found these floats to bob incessantly with regular up-and-down swings of about 10 feet. Similar movements were found in the Atlantic east of Bermuda and at the Equator, with violent internal Atlantic waves measuring 40 to 50 feet, and occasionally as high as 100 feet.

Dr. Theodore Pochapsky, who developed the floats, explained that the surveys are planned to explore both areas which have no internal waves and areas where they are unusually strong. "It will be interesting to see," he said, "what sort of underwater breakers form when 100-feet high 'internal wave' swells hit the continental shelf 50 miles or so away from our eastern coast."

The floats may also be used to study strange undersea "tides" and "weather" produced by rapid shifts in the flow of masses of cold or warm water deep beneath the ocean's surface.

"Rivers of Mud"

Somewhat related perhaps are mammoth "sea channels" carved out of the sea bottom by gigantic "rivers of mud." Findings of the Coast and Geodetic Survey's oceanographic vessel *Pioneer* 2 miles below the Bay of Bengal, Indian Ocean, reveal channels 4 miles wide and 300 feet deep. Scientists estimate the largest channel carried a volume of water 25 times greater than that of the Mississippi River. What triggers these sudden avalanches of mud at the bottom of the sea is not known.

Then there are "tidal waves," a misnomer, because the waves referred to have nothing to do with the tide. These so-called tidal waves should be termed *seismic sea waves,* or by their Japanese name of *tsunamis,* for they originate in jarring dislocations of the ocean floor and are caused by earthquakes. These rare events are dangerous because their origins are completely unpredictable, although the modern Seismic Sea Wave Warning System, operated by several cooperating countries, now predicts the arrival times of tsunamis at distant points in the Pacific, chief source of these waves.

Although tsunamis travel at high velocity in the deep ocean (600 feet per second), they are seldom felt on the open sea. But when they reach continental shelves, or a shore, the on-rushing water piles up with disastrous effect. Pressure waves also break away from a tsunamis, moving at high speed, and can be detected by sonar (see also Chapter V).

Drift Bottles Valuable

For centuries the idea of a bottle with a message in it being tossed from a ship or island or beach and washed up onto some far distant shore has brought with it thoughts of mystery and adventure, and even romance. Picking the bottle up and noticing a message within, the excited finder may wonder, as he fumbles over the cork, where had it come from? Who sent it? What dire circumstances may have cast it adrift? What mysterious ocean-river or current eddy carried it from its launching point to where it is now stranded?

Often the bottle and its message may be just a prank, dropped overboard after a festive evening on shipboard. Sometimes a postcard is asked to be returned as a souvenir of an ocean cruise. Some drift bottles now contain advertising, the owners hoping that the publicity may reach newspapers or other media. Other messages are obviously the work of cranks.

Now oceanographers are using drift bottles as a tool for studying ocean currents and patterns of ocean drift. Many bottles are released at specified locations in the oceans and when they are recovered, their possible routes are studied and the speed of the journey is determined. Bottles are used because: (1) they are relatively inexpensive, (2) they can be cast adrift from a moving ship, or one "on station" and need not be followed or tracked, and (3) when a large number of bottles are launched over a big area, the individual returns can be analyzed to give a synoptic or group picture of the surface currents for that area.

How Public Can Help

The Coast and Geodetic Survey began releasing messages in drift bottles in the fall of 1959 and has been using them regularly ever since. Other organizations have had drift bottle programs for many years; Woods Hole Oceanographic Institution has released them for 30 years as accepted instruments of scientific endeavor.

Bottles used by the Coast and Geodetic Survey are ordinary soft drink bottles containing the Coast and Geodetic Survey flag and an instructive legend painted on it. Inside are two cards. One explains why the bottle is there and what the Coast and Geodetic Survey hopes to learn from its travels; the other is a numbered prepaid postcard, asking the finder to complete information about when and where the bottle was found, and mail it with his name and address. The same are in English, French, Spanish, Portuguese, and Russian. When a card is returned, information on it is logged in and compared with a number recorded when the bottle was released. Then a letter is sent to the finder of the bottles, to let him know when and where it was released. Many people like these letters for their scrapbooks, or to discuss with friends.

What is the chance of a drift bottle card completing a round trip? Average total returns are about 8 per cent. Highest returns—52 per cent—came from a project near Martha's Vineyard, Massachusetts. At the other end of the scale, several projects out in the open ocean have had fewer than 1 per cent returns—although some of the bottles, lodged in rocks or fjords, may yet show up.

Plastic Bags and Other Drifters

In recent years there have been variations of the project, with drift cards and sea bottom drifters appearing on the scene. Drift cards are merely the same type of cards used in the bottles, enclosed instead in a plastic bag. The thin bag is weighted with a washer, so that most of the bag floats under the surface of the water. Cards in plastic bags are much easier to store and to handle than are bottles.

For studying bottom currents a different drifter was developed. This bottom drifter looks like a small mushroom with a long stem. The heavier stem rides beneath the lighter mushroom and keeps the mushroom 2 or 3 feet off the floor of the ocean. These drifters are sometimes washed up on shore, but more often are caught in lobster pots or in nets. Either way, they give an indication of the currents close to the sea bottom.

Drift bottles or bags can tell us many things. For example, the routes and meanderings of surface ocean currents can be fairly well followed. Often, previous theories about currents are reinforced, such as when the Gulf Stream carries a bottle to the west coast of Europe. Sometimes previously unknown currents are discovered or hinted at by the drift bottle's travel. At other times, drift bottle return data may be correlated with surface temperature and/or salinity data in a given area, to obtain a better interpretation of currents—so important to shipping, navigation, fisheries, and military defense.

The Sea and "Sevens"

In mythology and in many tales about the open sea, "seven" is a magic number. Novices proclaim that the seventh wave is always a *big* one; they have proved it at the seashore! Sometimes large waves do roll in at regular intervals, but not because an occasional one is stronger than another in the same series. The origin of such larger waves is generally outside *swell*—the waves from distant storms—which may arrive from two or more directions, depending upon the result of storms in different parts of the ocean. They occasionally upset the regular sequence of ordinary waves, but just as often at eight or nine intervals as seven.

Actually the number "seven" does have some authority in the science of the sea. Whatever the wind action, the ratio of wave height to the wave length (called wave steepness) theoretically cannot exceed one to seven, although it may in the immediate wave-generating area. When wave steepness reaches beyond one to seven, the wave usually breaks or forms whitecaps, which dissipate some energy by turbulence.

Scientists have found that the generation or building up of water waves is dependent on the transfer of energy from the wind to the water, and all wave forecasting and hindcasting techniques are primarily based on the correlation between wind, fetch (the distance the waves have run under the drive of the wind), wind duration, and the waves obtained by observations and recordings. The exact mechanism of wave growth under wind action is not completely known to man because individual wave-heights, and also the wave periods, vary.

As a curious footnote about "sea-sevens," the whale contains seven vertebrae in its back. Even more remarkable, however, is the fact that the lofty, dry-land giraffe has seven vertebrae in its neck. And so do people!

CHAPTER IV

THE LIVING WATERS—
FISHES AND MAMMALS

SEA LIFE, except in the extreme depths, is far more abundant and varied than life on land. From microscopic plankton, the basic food of the oceans, to huge whales, largest of living creatures, the sea still presents an enormous challenge and an enigma.

All living things of any size on land are known, and they have been studied and classified; this is not so in the sea. Hardly a year passes without some new species or specimens being disclosed. Some are brought up in nets, some in deepsea dredges, and a few in the stomachs of other fish. But many species must still be at large, considering the number of unknowns that come up at frequent intervals, despite the inevitable slowness of nets and trawls.

Modern submarine photographs have revealed many unknown creatures still uncaught. These await the refinements of new bathyscaphs and other equipment that man can manipulate face to face with the creatures of the depths.

End of Plant Life

Meanwhile, marine biologists will find much to study and many things to discover among those myriad creatures that live in the ocean, particularly those from the surface down to 600 feet, or 100 fathoms. Here is the realm of plant life; all animals below that depth live largely on each other. You will hear reference to the greatest depth of the sun's rays at 1,000 feet, but from 600 feet to 1,000 feet down such rays can be found only by instruments. Actually most living things begin to taper off at the edge of the continental shelves, which in Atlantic waters drop off sharply at about 70 fathoms, or 420 feet.

All of these vital statistics are of great importance to

biologists studying the inhabitants of the sea. Depth may change temperatures, and the range is especially important because few marine organisms have any mechanism for regulating their own temperature. Unlike certain land animals, which can add fur or fat or feathers to resist cold, and later shed them to meet warmer conditions, fish must run to find comfort.

The only consolation for fish is that the sea is never quite as warm (hottest ocean water is found in the Persian Gulf, where 96° Fahrenheit has been recorded), nor as cold (water temperature in polar seas drops to 29° F.) as what land creatures must endure. The deep sea, 9,000 feet and ocean floor below, is always 37.4° F.

Fish Like It Cold

Yet, surprisingly enough, sea life, in its most bewildering abundance, is generally in the colder, rather than the warmer seas. This is because the seasonal overturn of water temperatures in the cooler areas brings up minerals and tiny creatures from the bottom. Surface waters in polar and north temperature zones support immense swarms of plankton, the food for herring, mackerel and scores of other living sea creatures. Also, because fewer larval stages are found in cold surface waters, organisms tend to be less widely dispersed by the currents.

Although cold water supports immense numbers of fish individuals and relatively few species, conditions in tropical seas are almost the reverse. Here one discovers a rich and bewildering variety of species, not one of which is represented by any really large number of individuals. Why is this anomaly? The simplest explanation is that warm waters speed reproductions and help to produce many generations in the time required to produce one in the Arctic. Genetic variations are developed and established more rapidly, therefore.

But don't chalk this up as a rule. Some areas in the tropics are exceptions against teeming warm concentrations of life. Certain equatorial areas, such as those along the western coast of South America, upwell from deep, cold waters below and bring to the surface waters rich in minerals and many kinds of sea life. These definitely, however, are exceptions rather than the rule.

Living Chain of the Sea

If we are to begin at the living chain of the sea, we must start with the sunlit upper layers, where rich minerals fall from above and surge up from the depths. From sunlight and minerals, the plants of the sea, some so small as to be invisible to the unaided eye, make up the carbohydrates essential to animal life.

Now go another step up the biological ladder and identify the simplest and yet the most important vegetation available to the animals of the sea—the diatoms, tiny, single-celled plants. Under the microscope, their delicate structures look like two pieces precisely fitted, such as a box and its lid.

In early spring, especially in the temperate zone, the growing warmth of the ocean creates an immense upsurging of these creatures, a veritable blooming of the sea resulting from the sun and fertilizing minerals that churn up from the depths. Sometimes diatoms may cover immense areas, like a living undulating island, as they multiply and expand. Among them you may find other simple creatures. Protozoa, for instance, single-celled animals of curious shapes, feeding on microscopic vegetables. In turn, they provide the food for scores of other tiny things, such as clear worms, gnomelike crustacea, or minute jellyfish. Mixed among them may be the very young of fish, lobsters, crabs, shipworms, clams, and other miniature animals making their hazardous origins in the open sea.

Plankton, the "Wanderer"

Taken together, this drifting, teeming life of the sea is known as plankton, from the Greek for "wanderer." These upper waters of the ocean are extremely important as the source of much of the food of larger creatures, ranging from such moderate-sized fishes as herring, codfish, menhaden, and haddock to such huge denizens of the sea as the basking shark and the baleen whale.

In the sea, as on the land, the life cycle is supported by sunlight through a process known as photosynthesis. This earliest combination of elements is formed with the aid of radiant energy from the sun. To break down the pastures of the sea further, its one-celled chlorophyll-bearing plants are called phytoplankton. They in turn become the food of herbivorous zooplankton, the free-floating or weakly-swimming animals of many shapes and sizes. In sequence, the latter feed the carnivores of the ocean, the little ones being eaten by the big fishes and marine animals.

Death and decomposition complete the cycle. The organic material of both plants and animals is subjected to bacterial decay which releases again the carbon, phosphorous, and nitrogen needed for photosynthesis—all of which brings us back to where we came in. Because organic matter sinks, much of the decomposition occurs in deep water, well below the sunlit areas in which photosynthesis must take place. However, the essential elements are eventually returned to the surface by oceanic circulation, wind, and currents mixing the water column or upwelling the column.

Life Also in Depths

Light sufficient for photosynthesis can penetrate only to depths of about 300 feet, in even the clearest ocean waters; there is generally less penetration near shore, due to murky sediments washed from the land. While abundant phytoplankton can survive only in these shallow layers, some kind of animal life has been found in all parts of the ocean, even at the bottom of the deepest trenches, where the pressure is enormous.

How are the various concentrations of marine life in the sea studied? The Woods Hole Oceanographic Institution, for instance, defines four main areas: (1) ecology, the mutual relations between organisms and their environment; (2) the feeding, migration and distribution of zooplankton; (3) the dynamics and breeding cycle of sedentary bottom populations; and (4) the life cycle and distribution of pelagic (open sea, except bottom dweller) fishes. Laboratory and field investigations are still being made into effects of seasonal changes in temperature and salinity, or the importance of trace elements like iron and manganese in the lives of the phytoplankton. Relationships of this sort must be understood in order to make any kind of informed guesses about the eventual production of the ocean.

One of the biggest advances of recent years has been

the culturing of many species of phytoplankton so that they can be studied in controlled situations in the laboratory. Zooplankton are also being investigated in many ways. One group of scientists is interested in the effects of seawater in the man-made Cape Cod Canal, and of water life at both ends; another is studying samples collected under the Arctic ice by a nuclear submarine, hoping to determine where and how the Atlantic and Pacific populations are separated.

Light From Sea Animals

One of the most fascinating problems of the sea is bioluminescence ("phosphorescence" to landlubbers)—light produced by animals. How and why do the "fireflies of the sea" do it? What prompts their increased flashing at night—or is the increase only apparent?

In any event, some fishes can live in complete darkness and produce their own illumination by flashing rows of lights like those of miniature ocean liners, or they can turn on and off torches that eject clouds of glowing material. Some dangle lamps over their heads to lure prey. The deep sea, says Dr. George L. Clarke, of Harvard, "is not continuously enveloped in inky blackness, but, at times at least, must present the appearance of the night sky on the Fourth of July!"

As a result of several recent investigations of bioluminescence, scientists have added much to our knowledge of the subject. They began with the cold glow of the firefly and other living organisms which transform chemical energy into light. By probing the processes by which they obtain light, dissipating very little heat, scientists are learning also more about the ways in which living cells transform food into useable energy.

Through the mechanism provided by the U.S.-Japan Committee on Scientific Cooperation, and with the aid of a grant from the National Science Foundation, studies will continue on the biological and chemical nature of reactions that permit certain animals in the sea to create their own light. Much of the work involves a tiny crustacean known as *Cyprindina*. It was isolated at Princeton by a guest scientist, Dr. Osamu Shimomura of Nagoya University. He crystalized *Cyprindina* "luciferin"—the light-emitting substance that reacts with the enzyme luciferase to produce light—for the first time.

Used by Japanese During World War II

Cyprindina was well known to many Japanese soldiers during World War II for its light-producing qualities. In lieu of flashlights, they would crush and dry quantities of the small creature, then carry the powder with them at night. When water was added to a small amount of the powder in a soldier's palm, enough low-intensity safe light was produced to enable him to read maps or messages.

Another familiar example of bioluminescence is the "burning of the sea" in tropical waters. Myriads of organisms, often one-celled, emit this eerie "cold" light when stimulated by the movement of fish or other marine life, boats, oars, and even human arms or legs when immersed in such waters. The combined glow is often sufficiently bright to outline such objects.

Indeed, the range and diversity of bioluminescent organisms is impressive, including certain bacteria, fungi, sponges, jellyfish, crustaceans, snails, millipedes, and insects. Many fish, particularly in the deep sea, and lower forms of plant life, are luminous, but oddly enough there are no bioluminescent amphibia, reptiles, birds, or mammals.

Transfer of Energy

Basic research in bioluminescence is of interest not only in itself, but also as an avenue to one of the many enzymatic processes by which energy is transferred within cells. Thus, basic research in bioluminescence can provide answers to questions involving the transfer of energy within living organisms. Biochemists now know some of the components necessary for this highly efficient reaction, in which a large percentage of the chemical energy expended is transformed into light. However, they do not know exactly what triggers the reaction. Nor, in many cases, do they know the structure and proportion of the reactants.

Although most bioluminescent organisms emit light of only one color, some like the "railroad worm" are two-tone—with green lights on the side and gaudy red headlamps. Many bioluminescent organisms probably use their self-generated lights as signals, in their mating ritual, or as lures to attract food. The intensity of luminescence under the sea on some occasions approaches that of moonlight; as many as 100 bioluminescent flashes per minute have been recorded, and at depths as great as 2⅓ miles. A special camera, used to cause luminescent animals to take their own pictures, photographed a rare jellyfish at a depth of 3,000 feet.

Gamefisherman Taking Part

The amazing schooling habits of fishes also need much more scrutiny. One approach observed their behavior under experimental conditions, with their eyes shaded or covered by contact lenses; this has required still other studies, such as the optical properties of fish eyes. Those roving nomads of the sea—tuna and other gamefish—are being investigated by an extensive tagging program in which hundreds of sportfishermen from Miami to Nova Scotia are taking part, along with intensive long-line fishing operations.

Whales and porpoises have also been recruited in the search for information about the physiology and habits of the mammals of the sea. Sounds made by these creatures, formerly neglected, are now being studied at sea and in laboratories; it has been found that porpoises navigate with sonarlike devices and use sound for communication in several ways. Despite the difficulties of positive identification, a library of whale and porpoise sounds is being recorded.

Whales may have generated the intense, subsonic throbbings that oceanographers first detected in parts of the Atlantic and Pacific Oceans about a decade ago. In 1954 Bell Laboratories' oceanographers, studying acoustical problems in the North Atlantic, detected subsonic sounds (sounds with such low frequencies that humans cannot hear them) so energetic that they often rose 30 to 40 decibels above the level of the background noise. The sources of the sounds moved about randomly, at speeds varying between 2 and 8 knots and they were point sources, rather than extended sources, such as surf pounding on a beach.

The regularity of the pulses suggests that the sounds originated as the by-product of a biological process, such as heartbeat or breathing. The fact that the trains of pulses last for many minutes, halt, and then resume, seems to correspond to the traveling and feeding habits of whales. The next logical step should be positive identification of whales as the sources of the sounds—a difficult task, for as researchers in the field have noted, "a live whale in the water is an imposing experimental subject."

A "Dinner Bell" for Sharks

Because underwater animal sounds could be valuable aids in solving some of the secrets of undersea warfare and defense, a number of research investigations tracking strange sounds in the sea have been supported by the National Science Foundation. One project enlists sharks. Tracking his quarry by plane, a University of Miami scientist has found evidence indicating that sharks can use underwater sound waves to "home in" on a suspected food source—possibly including human beings—with remarkable speed and accuracy.

This follows an earlier discovery that a struggling fish or a threshing swimmer generates a "dinner-bell" sound wave—announcing his presence and location to the cruising shark. The findings resulted from a continuing study of hearing and related senses in fishes being conducted by Dr. Warren J. Wisby, of the University of Miami's Institute of Marine Science. His investigations could serve as a basis for understanding the amazing ability of fish to orient themselves in an environment that, to most humans, seems without landmarks.

Sharks tested by Dr. Wisby could detect and locate the source of low-frequency sound waves when cruising over 200 yards from the sound source—far beyond visual range and with no blood in the water for sharks to smell. Sharks up to 14 feet long have repeatedly been attracted by broadcasting underwater taped signals of pulsed low-frequency sounds. A light plane was used to find and track sharks, and a surface vessel transmitted the artificial "dinner call" sound wave.

More About Sharks

Biologically, the shark deserves a book in itself, because, in addition to its reputed sinister role as a man-killer, the creature is an extraordinary oddity. Some sharks bear young and others develop from eggs, some are ferocious and others cowardly, and, while it leaves no skeleton other than its jaws and teeth, shark teeth are among the oldest relics known to the sea. While a few marine specialists say that the shark has been badly maligned as dangerous, most experts agree that when a shark is hungry, nothing will stop it—including any fear of man. Man's acceptance of the shark's bloodthirsty reputation often breeds panic in its presence, and it is this which brings on attacks. Yet few live sharks have been kept long in captivity, such as tanks in aquariums, and the reason given is that they are too sensitive!

While not all attacks on man in the sea by marine creatures can be attributed to sharks—barracudas, moray eels, conger eels, urchins, lion fish, and others also injure humans—reputable observers report that human injuries from sharks have increased in recent years. This is not necessarily because the shark population has increased, but because more and more people now go into the sea for sports, research, and exploration.

These activities, plus the need of safety for those forced into the ocean by plane crashes (including an American astronaut, who had to bail out of his sinking capsule), have stepped up studies for an effective shark repeller. One such device, an electronic unit, operates on batteries housed in a waterproof casing from which extend two miniature antennas. Weighing about 4 pounds, it is small enough to be attached to skin-diving equipment or rubber rafts used by ditching planes or boats. It operates on the principle that electronic pulses at the proper rate, duration, and amplification can be tuned in on a shark's nervous system and send the shark off threshing wildly. The repeller is said to be effective up to 75 feet in all directions and lasts for several hours.

Fishermen, who lose thousands of dollars by sharks entangled in nets, would like to attach such a repeller to their boats and nets, to keep sharks and other predators away. The armed forces, the Coast Guard, and the National Aeronautics and Space Administration are also interested. As one NASA astronaut observed: "I'd hate to go into orbit only to splash into the sea and get eaten by a shark. What an anticlimax!"

Shark Search Panel

Meanwhile a host of shark repellants of various kinds have been placed on the market; so many, in fact, that a panel of distinguished scientists agrees that a full-scale federal program to investigate and regulate commercial deterrants is needed. The Shark Search Panel of the American Institute of Biological Sciences, meeting in Washington (November 1964) said that existing shark repellants are not effective against some types of sharks—one repellant was found to discourage lemon sharks but to *attract* tiger sharks. Scientists on the panel want the Federal Trade Commission, or the Food and Drug Administration, or some other reliable agency to take over the job of policing the devices and formulae.

Repellants are included today in the survival kits of Navy and Air Force men. The Navy, for instance, uses a repellant called "Shark Chaser," a purplish dye that, when spread over the water, confuses the sharks and keeps them away. Dr. S. R. Galler, head of the Biological Sciences Division of the Office of Naval Research, told the panel that no repellant is effective against *all* types of shark under *all* conditions—mainly because not enough is known scientifically about sharks.

Cetacean Research, Too

Likewise, not too much is known about the biological habits of whales, although whaling is one of the oldest seafaring activities. The first meeting on Cetacean—the technical collective term for whales and porpoises—research was held in 1963 at Rosslyn, Virginia, which is the head of tidewater of the Potomac River, opposite Washington, D.C. and normally not a haunt for cetaceans. Again the meeting was sparked by the American Institute of Biological Sciences, under the sponsorship of the Biological branch of the office of Naval Research.

Why is the Navy interested in cetaceans? Because the porpoise, in particular, is an animal which not only has a sophisticated detection system but also has an efficient, silent propulsion system, and the ability to dive and surface rapidly. Deeper knowledge of how the porpoise accomplishes these tricks could lead eventually to new concepts in electronics or mechanical equipment that would be an improvement on present navigation and detection systems, needed in submarine and antisubmarine warfare.

The Navy is also interested in cetacean studies because various living organisms, including bats, birds, and marine animals, have a remarkable ability to detect and identify targets and to travel great distances toward these targets, some in the air and some in the sea. Rear Admiral L. D. Coates, USN, then Chief of Naval Research, mentioned in his opening remarks at the symposium: "In recent years the Navy has come to realize that porpoises have capabilities and mechanisms for rapid swimming and diving navigation and underwater identification considerably superior to anything yet devised by man."

Scattering Layer

One of the most puzzling of all combinations of sea sounds is a "silent one" that comes to us through hydrophones. These are the mysterious "scattering layers" which were discovered by American scientists taking soundings off California during the early 1940's. Drifting at a depth of a quarter of a mile or more by day, these moving sea carpets tend to rise into surface waters at night. It baffled scientists and especially wartime physicists testing underwater sound as a tool for finding enemy submarines. Echo soundings in certain areas could mistake the layer for shoals; a ship passing through the same region at another time would find only deep water.

In search of the sound-scattering "animals," both TV cameras and still cameras met failures.

The sound reflecting zones do not seem dense enough for meaningful pictures. Reports Vincent J. Marteka, in *Sea Frontiers*, (May 1964):

> "After looking at a series of blank photographs taken with a camera lowered into a DSL (deep scattering layer), one disappointed scientist said it was like aiming a camera skyward and periodically clicking the shutter in the hope of photographing a stray bird in flight!
>
> "Perhaps the most exciting discovery in many years of DSL research occurred when Navy oceanographer Dr. Barham saw ghost-like figures while passing through a

DSL in the bathyscaph *Trieste*. The animals he saw were siphonophores—many-armed, largely transparent creatures common to warm seas. The particular siphonophores seen by Dr. Barham are similar to the Portuguese man-of-war and occur as colonies more than two feet long."

Gas-Filled Bladders

Dr. Barham further believes that gas-filled chambers or bladders of siphonophores reflect sound. When inflated, the bags are buoyant and cause the animal to rise; the animal may sink by expelling gas by muscular contraction. Siphonophores therefore are probably the primary cause of the originally discovered DSL, as well as of similar layers found throughout the warm water oceans of the world.

Whatever their identities, the deep scatterers play an important part in the great food chain of the oceans, forged as it is from animals ranging from tiny plankton to the giant whales. The deep scatterers are probably the middlemen, which rise to the surface in the evening to feed on small plankton; large fish and mammals in turn prey on them.

Even tinier than any of these, however, is a primary "population" of nonliving organic particles, constantly being created on air bubbles in the sea. This vast unsuspected food supply for marine life was only recently (1964) discovered by three U.S. scientists. Based on this research, one of these scientists also finds support for a "community" theory of evolution—according to which short-term advantages to individual species are sacrificed for long-term benefits for an entire living community.

Source of "Marine Snow"

Still more intriguing is a theory derived from this basic link in the marine food chain by a fourth marine biologist, who believes this research may also offer insight into the process by which life originally evolved from nonliving organic matter in the sea.

The joint discoveries were made by Dr. Gordon Riley, Yale University; Dr. E. R. Baylor, Woods Hole Oceanographic Institution; and Dr. William H. Sutcliffe, newly appointed director of the Marine Science Center at Lehigh, who conducted their research under grants from the National Science Foundation. Dr. P. J. Wangersky, of Yale, used the research of these three to arrive at a new insight into a possible origin of life itself—the prime mystery of the universe.

The tiny blobs of organic material, Dr. Riley believes, are the strange "marine snow" often reported but never understood by bathyscaph operators and marine scientists. Until now, most oceanographers have held that the marine food chain was a one-way process in which *life was derived only from life*. Small creatures were eaten by larger ones, and although dead remains might sink into deep water and serve as a food supply for deep sea creatures, it was thought that this dead material had to be decomposed to organic elements before it could again enter into the life cycle. Phytoplankton, the tiny *plants* of the sea, which assimilate these inorganic chemicals and use them for the production of living matter, were believed to be the sole source of food for the tiniest *marine* animals, the zooplankton.

Long-held Belief Untenable

Dr. Riley reasons that this long-held belief is untenable. Phytoplankton, he points out, grow only near the surface of the ocean and become very scarce in the winter when less radiant energy from the sun reaches the tiny plants. Modern marine surveys indicate that the amount of phytoplankton in the sea during winter months could not possibly support the acknowledged abundance of marine life in the oceans. Also, zooplankton grow and multiply in dark deep water beyond the depth attained by the tiny plants. Therefore, he contends, there must be another basic food supply in the ocean.

The breakthrough came when Drs. Baylor and Sutcliffe demonstrated in the laboratory that organic particles are continually being created in the ocean by the process of adsorption to air bubbles. Part of this organic particulate matter is converted inorganic matter formed by the action of bacteria, but a sizeable portion remains available as a stable food source for zooplankton.

Thus, the scientists contend, "there exists a vast reservoir of dissolved organic matter from which is created a 'population' of non-living matter that is more stable than the living population of phytoplankton. The reservoir of dissolved organic matter is constantly replenished by decaying organisms, and organic secretions from phytoplankton and zooplankton."

Clues to Origin of Life

In a further sidelight, Dr. Wangersky believes that this mechanism of adsorption by bubbling may be an important step in the long process of evolution from inorganic chemicals in the sea. If this be true, said Dr. Wangersky, we owe our very existence to organic particulate matter, for organic aggregates formed on air bubbles might be the progenitors of all life, including man.

"Even if life did not trace its ancestry back to air bubbles in the sea," Dr. Riley adds, "it seems certain that if a stable marine food supply created from a vast reservoir of dissolved organic matter did not exist, there would be less life today and fewer stable forms. Probably most deep sea life would be non-existent, since organic particulate matter appears to be their basic food source."

Not So Silent Depths

Switching to another unusual phase of the biological sea, perhaps there is no greater misnomer than the familiar "silent depths of the ocean." Wherever there is life in the sea, which means most of the time, its waters resound with a multitude of calls and cries. Different creatures make different noises, some to attract each other, some to warn off enemies, others perhaps just for the joy of making a clatter. Turn on a hydrophone and listen to the voices of the depths—grunts, squeaks, pops, clicks, and whistles. Some creatures make a sound like fat frying in a griddle; others give out a distinct heavy knocking, as if a lost soul were trying to gain release from Davy Jones' Locker!

Shrimp emit a crisp snapping noise. Porpoises are positively weird with their excited cries, as are also certain whales. The purpose of the porpoise is not only to avoid reefs and other obstacles to its speedy course but also to capture fish, which it does by sending out a continuous flow of underwater pulses, guiding itself to its prey by the running echoes. The reaction simulates sonar, or the animal radar used by bats while flying at night or in pitch-dark caverns. Such sea sounds may also hold small schools together to escape capture individually.

Although much research has been done on sea noises with hydrophones, and many different sounds have been recorded, until recently it was possible to identify only a few of them with the fish or mammal involved. Then, in 1962, off Bimini, the Bahamas, the first underwater audio-visual research facility was able to obtain *simultaneous* sight and sound studies of marine life from its natural environment on the sea bottom. Both sound and pictures came in clearly in this pioneer TV program, "live" from Neptune's realm.

Why was Bimini selected for this project? The first reason is that seawater in the Bahamas is probably the clearest in the world, affording good sighting conditions; the second is that the Straits of Florida (Gulf Stream) contain a large and varied sea life, permitting a wide range of observations and sound studies. This is important also because one of the major phases of the project was to help the Navy to distinguish biological sea sounds from ship sounds, in the detection of marauding enemy submarines.

Two Marine Facilities at Hand

In addition, two excellent marine facilities were at hand for the operation. The Lerner Marine Laboratory has there its tropical adjunct of the American Museum of Natural History, and the equipment for the test could be easily brought from the nearby Institute of Marine Science of the University of Miami, Florida. Both institutions supplied personnel.

The project had two major units—one under the sea, and another linked with a laboratory ashore by a coaxial cable. The sea operation contained a single closed-circuit television camera, installed in conjunction with underwater hydrophones at a depth of 65 feet, about a quarter mile west of Bimini. The hydrophones were set up at the points of a triangle to permit positive location of sound sources by triangulation. Floodlights on the bottom permitted night and cloudy day observations. By cable, the operations were easily observed in a room of the Lerner Laboratory, where both pictures and sound were recorded for future use.

There were other possible dividends, such as observations of animal reactions to sounds of various kinds, because the new Bimini facility can *send out*, or produce sounds, as well as *pick them up*. This study could also supplement work now being done on the repelling of venomous and carnivorous fish. Other plans call for a definition of target echoes to prevent false target interpretations by active sonar in submarine and antisubmarine warfare.

Hunt for Small Giants

Although sports fishermen generally try for the *biggest* game in capturing tuna, marlin, swordfish, and sailfish, scientists are seeking for specimens of the *smallest* of these giant creatures. It is not easy to do, because such pelagic, or open sea, fishes spend their time, from birth to death, far from land. Recently a major expedition of marine biologists aboard the *R/V John Elliott Pillsbury,* Institute of Marine Science, Miami, took a 21-day oceanographic cruise to Bermuda, the Sargasso Sea, and the northeastern Bahamas, to trace the life histories, migration patterns, and spawning locations of large oceanic fishes. Larval specimens were taken, including the white marlin and the blue marlin, some of them approximately ⅛ inch in length (believed to be the smallest marlin of both species ever caught), broadbill swordfish as small as ¼ inch in length, and many larval dolphin, barracuda, and giant ocean sunfish of about the same tiny lengths.

Hundreds of larval tuna were also taken. According to Dr. Donald P. de Sylva, field party chief, the tuna larvae comprise one of the most extensive collections of young tuna ever assembled. Such plankton collections established the fact that major spawning grounds of marlin are located southwest of Bermuda, and in the northeast and northwest Bahamas. Many unusual deep-sea animals were captured alive and photographed, including the extraordinary argonaut, the octopod that lives in the beautiful and rarely found nautilus shell. Two specimens were taken alive, and one, while being photographed in an aquarium, gave birth to hundreds of microscopic baby argonauts, complete with pearly transparent shells less than a millimeter in diameter.

Saving the Oyster

Ever since the first North American colonists arrived in the early 17th century they found that shellfish, mainly oysters, were abundant and had been used by aborigines for food long before the white man came. Molluscan shellfish were smoked and dried for barter with the inland Indians. A great American industry had its start in the 1830's in Maryland, when Baltimore oyster dealers began packing and shipping oysters refrigerated in ice.

However, about 1900, the oyster harvest began to decline. The reasons for the decline are many, and they reach beyond the purely biological to economic and social conditions that affect the national as well as the local industry. Problems of exploitation and pollution have also arisen. As a result, mass mortality of oysters in Delaware Bay and Lower Chesapeake Bay have now reached epidemic proportions, virtually wiping out the oyster industry in Delaware Bay and severely damaging the industry in Virginia.

The chief cause of these mortalities is as yet unknown, but there is evidence that an organism called MSX (multinucleate sphere unknown) may be the infective agency responsible. Phases of oyster disease research include diagnostic stain techniques for certain disease stages and an attempt to culture oyster cells for diagnosis of oyster diseases, much as human cells are now cultured for study of virus diseases.

Emergency Problems

Efforts of the Bureau of Commerical Fisheries and other federal shellfish research activities in Chesapeake Bay in the past have been somewhat sporadic and usually brought about by pressure from emergency situations—the blue crab distribution problem, the location and population density of oysters in the Potomac River, pulp mill effluents in the York River, and oyster mortalities in Mobjack Bay are examples. The present federal program began during the winter of 1943–1944 when Dr. Paul S. Galtsoff, then in charge of Shellfish Investigations, U.S. Department of the Interior, Fish and Wildlife Service, prepared a plan for cooperative oyster research in Maryland waters, which was accepted by Maryland authorities.

Present investigations, concerned directly with shellfish biology, ecology, and culture began in 1944 in Annapolis. Since 1960 the work has been based at a new laboratory built at Oxford, Maryland. More recently several studies affecting reproduction, growth, survival, recruitment, and genetics have been added to the program. Research is concentrated on the oyster, although studies are being conducted on hard and soft clams and the blue crab.

The Oxford laboratory, on the Tred Avon River of Chesapeake Bay, maintains a substation on seaside Chincoteague Bay as well as sampling facilities on the New Jersey coast. Field experiments conducted in Chesapeake Bay and at the Chincoteague substation are designed to detect and develop strains of oysters that are resistant to disease.

Pond Culture of Oysters

For several years, both abroad and in the United States, investigators have felt that a practical answer to oyster pollution and disease is the utilization of salt-water ponds, and methods similar to those used by the Japanese have been adopted. Initial studies at Oxford were so promising that more elaborate experiments have been started. In the spring of 1964 a rigid pier-like structure in Boone Creek, a natural salt-water pond adjacent to the laboratory in Oxford, was rigged with strings of seed oysters. Some 1,000 strings have been suspended and the staff anticipate that about 300 to 500 oysters will be harvested from these strings in the fall of 1965.

To complete this program, studies have begun on the culture of oysters in the four ¼-acre artificial salt ponds constructed at the Oxford laboratory. In these ponds many factors can be controlled, primarily the type of bottom most suitable for healthy oysters—bottoms with sand, oyster shell, polyethylene film or natural clay.

Growth and survival studies are already underway there, using oysters dredged in Broad Creek and moved to the ponds with the cooperation of the Maryland Department of Chesapeake Bay Affairs.

The Oxford oyster studies may not completely turn the tide of a once great industry. (Per capita consumption of oysters in the United States dropped from 3.09 pounds in 1880 to 0.24 pounds in 1963.) The combined efforts of science, industry, legislation, and advertising will be needed to make this fine natural food a product of more general use on the tables of our nation.

As stated by the famous scientist C. M. Yonge, in his book *Oysters* (London, 1960), ". . . the probability of a future for the oyster industry will be based largely on the results of intensive research at laboratories. . . ." With control of such environment factors as temperature, water salinity, amount and kinds of food organisms, predators, diseases, and pollution, oysters could be raised or farmed as successfully as many of the products grown on land. The use of both artificial and clean natural salt ponds may make this possible.

CHAPTER V

THE BOTTOM—AND LOWER!

MARINE GEOLOGY is a comparatively new member of the ocean-science family. Deep cores, unique dredging equipment, sampling devices, increased surveying of the ocean floor, and the probing of unknown abysses have opened up a host of new marine studies, as well as much technical work closely related to oceanographic research of the depths.

Only in fairly recent years have we had the stout lines or cables, the special drills, and the expert machinery required to investigate these nether regions. This new era may be said to have begun on a large scale when huge equipment, called "Texas Towers," were erected well beyond the shoreline. Here, on the continental shelves, the towers were erected to exploit oil and sulfur reserves under the sea. Then came heavier devices, working deeper, that could bring up such pure minerals as manganese, and even diamonds. Certain valuable ores are down there, too. Costly now, they will become relatively cheaper in the future as dwindling land resources force us to turn more and more to the sea to meet the growing demands of the world's exploding populations.

First Sample of the Mantle

Discovery that the earth's outer crust is thinner under the ocean than it is on land (where the weight of land mountains push the crust down) led to such daring enterprises as "Mohole," which hopes eventually to bring up, by means of the world's deepest cores, the first examples of the mantle—the largest and least known constituent of the earth. Tests have already shown that drilling may be done at sea from unanchored platforms—but more about the "Mohole" later.

Gradually marine geologists, by the use of modern science and engineering skill, are beginning to unveil the true origins of such geologic mysteries as deep sea canyons, the raw edges of the continental shelves, the extensive mountain ranges under the sea, the abyssal plains, the sources of guyots (flat-topped underwater peaks or mesas), the birth of atolls, and why odd nodules of solid metals are deposited on the bottom.

But many geological mysteries of the depths remain. Why, for instance, are large areas of the sea bottom covered deep in ooze and mud, while other regions are free of all sediment but sand and pebbles? Recent geologic studies have revealed that the layers of unconsolidated sediments in the deep sea are really quite thin—on the average only about 300 meters (1,200 feet) in thickness. Further, we have discovered there fossils only of Tertiary or Cretaceous ages (that is, under about 100 million years), but none older. Confirming this, but not explaining it, are the existing abyssal plains, all adjusted to recent topography; but where were the ancient abyssal plains?

Base of Crust Mystery

These are but a very few of the vast number of questions which confront students and researchers in this now-being-revealed submarine area. We still do not know, for instance, whether the base of the crust is in a phase of transition or if there is a real difference in chemical composition between the familiar crust and the yet unseen mantle. Are there pools or sheets of molten rock beneath the earth's crust, associated with inland trenches or fracture zones?

For that matter we know very little about the history of seawater itself, nor how the patterns of major ocean currents of the deep during past times compare with those of today.

Long before these costly studies need be considered, however, marine geology must gain certain immediate goals. A reasonable portion of the marine scientist's time and effort must be directed toward the numerous and more practical aims of the federal government, which supports and sponsors the major activity of oceanographic research today.

The reason for this situation is simple. Although most scientists would prefer to keep oceanography in the hands of private or educational institutions, or in research laboratories, or, at least, within a group of them, the needs for science have expanded enormously. Many new programs must be undertaken that are beyond the capacity of each institution to meet separately, or even as small groups. In short, the overall program needs certain federal guidance and, above all, money.

Broad Area Surveys

Among these guidance requirements are: (1) the maintenance of a complete library of oceanographic data; (2) the testing and calibration of a variety of instruments, including novel devices and experiments; (3) the forecasting of oceanic conditions of both research and operational interest; and (4) ice and wave forecasting. Two of these objectives, (1) and (2) above, have been launched in rebuilt buildings at the former Naval Weapons Plant, now renamed the Navy Yard Annex, in Washington, D.C.

But to return specifically to the needs of marine geology, both the scientific community, through the National Academy of Sciences Committee on Oceanography (NASCO), and several important federal agencies have expressed a strong and urgent desire for systematic mapping of the major properties of the oceans—the basins which contain them, sediments which lie under them, forces such as gravity and magnetism which permeates them, and the little-known bottom life they contain.

Mapping Program Enormous

Such undersea mapping can, of course, serve a wide variety of goals and purposes. It will provide tools for military use (undersea and antisubmarine warfare) and for economic welfare (minerals, ores, etc.), as well as for purely scientific aspects of oceanography, such as currents, counter-currents, marine life, bottom cores, etc.

The mapping of the bottom would alone be a truly staggering project, particularly beyond the rim of the continental shelves, and the cost would be enormous, even with echo devices. For, believe it or not, although we have mapped huge star charts millions of light years away, less than 5 per cent of the sea bottom of our own earth has been adequately surveyed. The United States will probably have to produce a major share of the work yet to be done, possibly a third of the total, but several other nations, including Russia, have promised to assist as their resources and manpower permit.

Most encouraging is the international armada of more than 40 vessels and scientists from 30 nations which joined the Indian Ocean Expedition, and the work of several nations and ships in the recent South Atlantic Expedition (International Cooperative Investigation of Tropical Atlantic). The focus of each of these groups was on fisheries and marine biology, but if such expeditions can move steadily ahead, despite tensions on both sides of the Iron Curtain, we have reason to believe that the mapping program needed in marine geology may be accelerated and the basic elements may be met, perhaps sooner than we now believe. The cost will be enormous; the total cost of the Indian Ocean project alone is expected to run

94 • NEW WORLDS OF OCEANOGRAPHY

to $260 million—a lot of money spent beyond anyone's territorial limits.

What is The Mohole Project?

Let us go from the general to something specific in marine geology. A prime example is the Mohole Project, which involves both pure and applied oceanic sciences, plus engineering and technical operations. In fact, if you mention the bottom of the sea to the average person today, nine out of ten times you will first be asked: "What is this Mohole we hear so much about?"

Perhaps because it is big and has captured the imagination of those accustomed to thinking in terms of huge rockets and long trips to outer space, the Mohole Project has received attention probably beyond its importance, when one considers the number of acute oceanic problems needing solution today. However, most oceanographers and marine engineers are justly proud of the daring and ingenuity that brought the first step of the Mohole into being. They hope that the project can be continued at not too great a cost, and without interfering with too many other important marine science and technological needs.

Meanwhile, Phase I of the Mohole Project is a fascinating story, the equal of exciting fiction. Let us recount its genesis. We must recall first that the interior of the earth is divided into a number of unequal zones or bands: (1) the outer shell, or crust; (2) the mantle; (3) the outer core; and (4) the inner core. The sum total of the four zones is roughly, from surface to center, 4,000 miles. We know very little about any of it except the thin outer shell, or crust.

Biggest Thing on Earth

Yet the unknown mantle is the biggest thing on earth. Of the total 4,000 miles between sea level and the center of the globe, the mantle alone covers almost half the distance, or some 1,800 miles. Although the mantle may have the answers to some of earth's innermost secrets, including the earthquake, no one has yet *brought up a piece of it*. Several scientists have guessed that the mantle may be a form of dunite or peridotite, the hard igneous rocks similar to stony meteorites that drop in from space, but they are not sure.

As for the zones *below* the mantle, the next or "outer core" is quite different, being fiery molten nickel-iron. This we know from volcanoes which spew it up to the surface from time to time, bringing with it fluid rock or lava. The innermost core, 850 miles thick, is believed to be of solid metal.

How do we know there is such a thing as the mantle? Who defined the boundary between it and the upper crust of the earth? Back in 1909 a Yugoslav seismologist named Andrija Mohorovicic detected a kind of break or borderline, roughly 18 to 30 miles below the earth's crust, while studying shock waves created by earthquakes. This distinct "acoustic boundary" behaved differently and thus indicated a variation in the material composing this part of the earth. This new boundary was at first called the "Mohorovicic Discontinuity" until someone luckily shortened it to "Moho." When the decision was made to attempt to drill into it, the name of the hole naturally became the "Mohole."

Why Sea, Not Land?

But the big question that puzzles everyone who hears about the Mohole for the first time is why do you have to drill through *deep sea bottoms,* instead of boring from *land*? On dry land wouldn't you have a stable platform, or rig, and ready access to pipe, lining, equipment, and manpower? Excellent questions, but the answer is that the mantle is not as deep down under the sea bottom as it is from the surface of the land.

Scientists have a word for this up-side-down situation, calling it isostasy. Like icebergs, which must extend well below the sea in order for a small portion to float above the surface, continents must be compensated for mountains which rise well above the ground. These masses of land rock push down the viscous body of the mantle. Seawater and the lighter basalt rocks of the ocean floor permit the mantle to rise.

Under the land crust of the continents, the mantle is at least 80,000 feet deep. Present equipment would not go down that far; it would simply break of its own weight. In fact, the deepest hole yet drilled on land is 25,340 feet deep, just a third of the land journey to the mantle. On the other hand, the outer crust under the sea is only 15,000 feet thick in places. Thus a Mohole 30,000 to 35,000 feet deep would have to be drilled only half the distance through sea water and soft clays and about half through rock before reaching the mantle itself.

Some Practical Aspects

Nevertheless, the Mohole, when it is finally accomplished, will be the deepest drilling operation in history. Even so, what is the purpose of it? The prime answer again is man's desire to know more about this globe on which he lives. Call it scientific interest and discovery, if you wish. However, it does have some practical aspects. The petroleum industry is interested in any methods of probing depths which might contain more reservoirs of oil. Recent discoveries have found valuable deposits of minerals on the ocean floor, but no economic methods of mining the deep deposits have yet been devised. An exception, however, are pockets of diamonds, recovered under the sea off South Africa (see Chapter VI). Naval engineers, who need more precise positions of ships at sea, will want to know more about the Mohole operations, wherever they take place.

Scientists are keeping close watch of future activities of Mohole for other scientific reasons. What is the earth made of? Why does the globe wiggle or jerk now and then—enough to force the observatories of the world to reset their clocks? When did life in the sea actually begin? Is there really a continuous drift of the continents? Is the earth getting warmer or colder; if so, which, and when will the effects begin and what will they mean to melting or freezing icecaps along the edges of the sea? Mohole may not have all the answers to these questions, but the queries are within the target area.

Scientists other than geologists and oceanographers are interested in the project. Paleontologists, for instance, have been unable to span the gap between the record of fairly simple Precambrian life and that of the relatively complex organizations that began to appear in the Paleozoic era. Perhaps longer cores penetrating deeper into the Moho may shed some light on these problems.

Catchall Group, Called AMSOC

So much for the theoretical background. What has been done about it? The record goes back to 1952, when the Office of Naval Research in Washington set up an informal section, where all the far-fetched, seemingly impractical, or crackpot schemes gravitated for final disposition. This catchall section had no name, but someone dubbed it the American Miscellaneous Society, or AMSOC for short. It had no officers, nor even a membership roll.

But what started out as more or less of a joke, soon found itself in deep water—that is, when AMSOC began to realize that the easiest method to reach the earth's hidden mantle is to drill a hole in the bottom of the sea. Who suggested the original idea, or exactly when, is not listed in the minutes—perhaps for the very good reason that no minutes were taken!

During the next nine years "Mohole" was tossed around over coffee and cigars, usually after more serious science meetings and seminars were ended. Finally in 1952, at an informal breakfast meeting in the home of Scripps Institution of Oceanography's Walter Munk, it was decided to set up a drilling committee—and "Project Mohole" was born. The roster reads like a Who's Who of some of the nation's leading oceanographers, geophysicists, geologists, and marine engineers. Chairman was Gordon Lill, head of the Geophysics Branch of the Office of Naval Research, and others included Dr. Roger Revelle, then director of Scripps; William W. Rubey, Harry S. Ladd, and Joshua I. Tracey, of the U.S. Geological Survey; Harry H. Hess of Princeton; Arthur E. Maxwell, of ONR; and Maurice Ewing, of the Lamont Geological Observatory, Columbia University.

First Formal Meeting

At the Project's first formal meeting, in the Cosmos Club, in Washington, D.C. enthusiasm grew as scientists of many disciplines pooled their ideas. "At long last," one of the group exclaimed, "the earth sciences, which include the sea, have something in glamour, daring and scope to match the efforts of rocketry and guided missiles." At last, gloated another, the Free World now has a chance to achieve *a real first in something big,* for Russia still has no competence in deep drilling, and particularly at sea.

To launch the Project properly, the AMSOC Mohole Committee was made an official committee of the top ranking National Academy of Sciences. Thus expense money could be granted through regular channels by the National Science Foundation. A select group of experts, under the guidance of Willard Bascom, chief engineer and director of the Mohole Project, was told to roll up its sleeves and get to work.

An Argosy Called "Cuss I"

It was decided that the initial operations at sea would be carried out in several phases. Phase I would be a feasibility test of deep sea drilling equipment and techniques. It was not intended to reach the mantle, and didn't. But the world's first deep sea drilling operation, from two sites, took place in March and April 1961. The locations were 16 miles west of La Jolla, California, and another 50 miles east of Guadaloupe Island, off the coast of Mexico. Its floating argosy was a converted Navy freight barge, renamed *"Cuss I,"* an abbreviation of the four oil companies (Continental, Union, Shell and Superior) for which it normally did exploratory drilling near the shore.

Almost as ugly as its unlikely name, barge *Cuss 1* nevertheless did a good job. Its 98-foot derrick withstood gale-force winds, and its stout hull supported a working load of 300 tons. There were racks for two miles of drill pipe in 60-foot sections. When the ship rolled or momentarily drifted off position, a heavy guide shoe, extending through a large hole in the barge's center, prevented excess bending of pipe. As for the lower end of the drill string, a flexible casing here cushioned any bending when the pipe entered the sea floor.

No Anchoring Possible

Then arose the question of holding the drilling rig in one spot. A number of anchoring devices were considered and discarded. Ships can be held in deep water usually with a dredging-winch cable; measure the angle of the cable, and use the ship's propeller and rudder cleverly, and a vessel can be *nearly* on station. But nearly on station is *not enough* when a couple of miles of pipe are dangling from the ship. The pipe would bend and break before drilling could commence.

This problem called for original thinking, and sure enough a new idea came up from Willard Bascom, the Project Director. He suggested "dynamic positioning." That is, hold the unanchored barge in one spot by sensing fixed markers. Then hold the barge there by means of "steering crews," or king-sized outboard motors rigged around the hull.

When a site at sea was selected, a series of anchors (old streetcar wheels) would be dropped from a ring or cat's cradle of taut-line buoys. Such lines and buoys would move very little with the current or wind. At the surface they would be rigged also with radar reflectors, and near the surface with underwater buoys, which would bounce back the "pings" of a sonar transducer on the barge.

"Joystick" Centers Outboards

Thus the pilot house can know the position of the barge at all hours of the day and night, in fair weather or foul. In the pilot house a small lever, like an early plane's "joystick," could change the thrust positions of the four big screws, swinging or moving the barge in any direction desired.

This unique arrangement worked very well in practice. As a double check on the positioning of the ship, however, and to reduce bending stresses in the drill pipe where it entered the bottom, a thin steel cable was dropped straight down to another anchor on the sea floor. An inclinometer was rigged just above the anchor, and, when the ship began to move off station, the cable pulled a tilt into the inclinometer.

Watch For That "Tilt!"

Similar to a "tilt" on a pinball machine, lights flashed up in the pilot house, until the barge was properly adjusted.

Sometimes the deep currents required that the ship take a position slightly upstream of the hole, so that the pipe could enter the bottom vertically.

While *Cuss I* will not be the vehicle finally used to reach the mantle, it did a fine job. Its diamond-studded, tungsten-carbide drills ground cut-cores from below 3,000 feet of water at La Jolla, with the drill bit reaching a maximum depth of 1,035 feet beneath the ocean floor. After five holes were dug there, the barge and its equipment were moved to a site off Guadaloupe Island, where another five holes were drilled in 11,700 feet of water, reaching a maximum of 601 feet below the ocean bottom.

What the Cores Revealed

Cores brought up quite a variety of consolidated fine sands and coarse silts with scattered fossil content. Geologists were excited particularly when the drill, at 760 feet off La Jolla, found carbonate-cemented rock, which X-ray analysis showed to be dolomite. Off Guadaloupe a cross section at 560 feet showed mainly green-gray ooze. Some of the ooze beds were microscopic shells of plants and animals, mixed with volcanic glass shards, ash, and clays. Other cores consisted of clay and volcanic ash. Most of these deposits were Miocene, that is 12 to 20 million years old.

Most significant of all this "Mohole" preliminary work was its attainment, for the first time in history, of the second or sub-layer of the earth's crust, which was penetrated 41 feet. While these cores proved to be only a common type of theoleitic basalt, two important geophysical measurements were made: (1) the seismic velocity of the sediments in Layer I was determined at 1.6 km/sec., much slower than previous estimates; (2) temperature measurements were made at different depths. Actual in-hole measurements at Guadaloupe indicated a slightly higher temperature than had been inferred. Still another first, was the simultaneous measurements of deep ocean currents at four levels.

While all of this may be rather confusing to the layman, these findings have value to the scientist, and study of them will continue in the laboratory. In addition, *Cuss I* yielded a great deal of technical experience necessary for

THE BOTTOM—AND LOWER! • 101

attaining the final objective—the *actual boundary* between the crust and the mantle of the earth.

What Lies Ahead

Meanwhile, two or three years of laboratory study, field tests, budget problems, and certain inevitable politics lie ahead before the major assault on the Moho can begin. For Phase II, also, newer, larger, and more costly equipment will be needed to operate a much longer drill string.

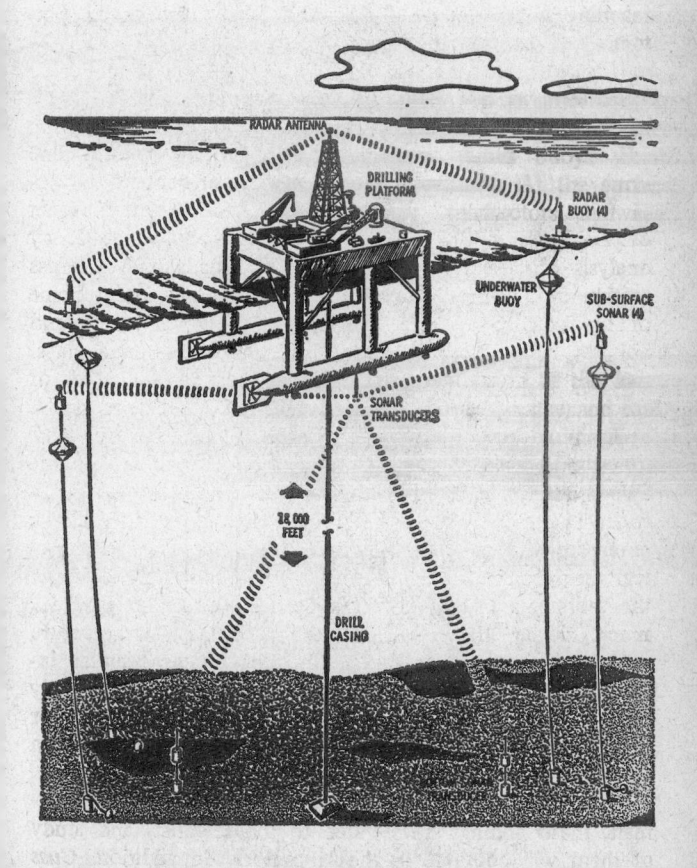

Mohole II diagram of drilling platform in the Pacific.

A bigger ship is the prime necessity—one that is specifically designed for the task, because it may have to remain on station at least a couple of years in all kinds of weather. Living quarters for at least 100 men, repair facilities, and scientific laboratories will be needed, plus even a compact saline water conversion plant, to assure fresh water at all times.

Early in 1964, a number of major changes in the organizations involved in the progress of Project Mohole took place. The National Academy of Sciences announced that the AMSOC Committee of the Academy, which initiated the Mohole Project, was disbanded. In transmitting its final recommendations to the Academy, the AMSOC group stated: "In order to take full advantage of the new developments in the National Science Foundation, we recommend that certain steps (above) be taken to increase the effectiveness of the Academy's advice. In making this recommendation, we are optimistic about the future."

Large Drilling Platform

The National Science Foundation, in announcing a program to proceed with Project Mohole, has listed a technical and operating plan involving a large floating drilling platform, equipped to carry out scientific drilling programs at intermediate depths prior to its use for the deep hole through the earth's crust to the mantle. Equipment capable of the latter task would be developed, too, during the intermediate drilling.

As presently envisioned, the lower platform will have two submersible submarine-like hulls, 390 feet long and 35 feet in diameter. Above them, on six 31-foot diameter columns, rests the upper platform, 279 feet long, 234 feet wide and 23 feet high. At a light draft of 28 feet, the platform will have a displacement of 13,500 tons. In this condition it can be moved to and from the drill sites, with the two lower hulls partially submerged. The two main propulsion units located at the stern of each hull will provide a cruising speed of 8 to 10 knots.

Hulls Submerged During Drilling

During drilling, the platform will have a displacement of 21,500 tons and draft of approximately 60 feet. Only

THE BOTTOM—AND LOWER! • 103

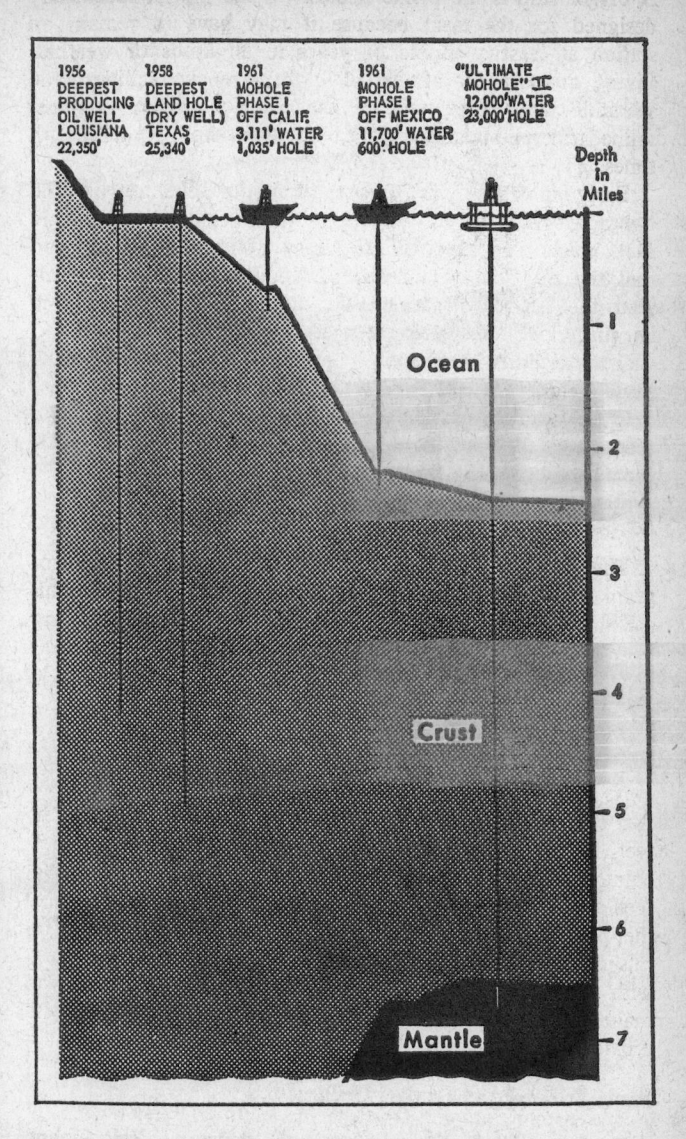

Chart of drilling depths to attain the mantle.
(National Science Foundation)

the six widely spaced columns will be exposed to wave action, as the two lower hulls will be fully submerged.

The platform will be positioned on station almost directly above the hole by six right-angle drive propellers, located just below each of the columns. Their direction and speed will be controlled by a computer that will take its position signals from underwater sonar equipment, similar to that used by U.S. Navy submarines. All machinery, living quarters, laboratories, and drilling equipment will be contained in or upon the upper hull. The twin lower hulls will be used for storing fuel, fresh water, and ballast. The drilling derrick will be located at the center of the platform, the position of minimum deck action.

The decision to design a platform, instead of a converted ship, was the result of experience during the past year, when several somewhat similar floating platforms were used by oil-drilling contractors in the Gulf of Mexico, sometimes during severe weather. In 1963 it was reported that one rig shut down for only seven days because of storms, although there were 79 days when wave heights reached from 10 to 29 feet. The roll and pitch of the platform during this period exceeded two degrees only when wave heights exceeded 20 feet.

A Dual Program

The platform will be used for a dual program: (1) test operations, and then (2) the drilling necessary to penetrate 15,000 to 20,000 feet of the earth's crust under 12,000 to 15,000 feet of water, for the final assault on the mantle. Use of an "intermediate" conventional vessel, for testing equipment and gaining drilling experience, was rejected partly because of the additional cost, but primarily because the platform, with its greater inherent stability, is expected to be a better base for carrying out all needed drilling system developments.

In January 1965 the National Science Foundation announced the location of the initial hole to be drilled to the mantle. The site is in the mid-Pacific Ocean, about 100 miles north-northeast of Maui, Hawaii. Seven other sites in the Pacific, ranging from as far south as Panama to the waters off Washington, have also been chosen for drilling in lesser depths for scientific research purposes.

Drilling To Take Three Years

Announcement of the initial drilling, a second major objective of the Mohole Project, was made jointly by the Foundation, the National Academy of Sciences-National Research Council, and Brown & Root, Inc., of Texas, the prime contractor. Drilling is expected to begin in 1968 and will take perhaps three years to reach its 6-mile-deep objective.

Drilling at the intermediate sites should begin within 1967, according to Gordon Lill, project director for the Foundation. These seven locations are: Mendocino Scarp (northwest of San Francisco), East of Cobb Seamount (west of Seattle, Washington), Cascadia Abyssal Plain (west of Seattle), San Diego Trough (off Los Angeles-San Diego), Cocos Ridge area (west of Panama), south of Maui (Hawaii), and a second site north of Maui (Hawaii). Dr. Harry H. Hess, of Princeton University, was chairman of the Mohole Site Selection Committee for the Academy of Sciences, and reviewed the data available to it on the various sites.

Cores From Project LOCO

Mohole is not the only project attempting to obtain deep sea cores. While not yet in the race for the mantle, preliminary drilling off Jamaica by the University of Miami's Project LOCO has brought some excellent cores from beneath the ocean floor in 2,000 feet of water. LOCO here means LOng COres, according to its sponsors, Drs. C. Emiliani and F. F. Koczy. Drilling from the Global Marine Exploration vessel *Submarex*, between Pedro and Walton Banks, southwest of Jamaica, total penetration into the ocean floor was 185 feet, with a total of 68 feet of cores recovered.

Three other locations were occupied, but the expedition was plagued by bad weather and equipment failures—including failure of a specially designed piston corer. Preliminary analysis shows that from the surface to a depth of 180 feet, the sediment appears to be a "sort of Globigerina ooze," light gray in color because of finely disseminated magnesium oxide.

Need for 'Quake Cores

Not all of the prime needs for oceanic cores are in studying the crust and the mantle, or in drilling for oil and minerals along the continental shelves. One reason why we have not yet found what happened on the Pacific Ocean floor during the great Alaskan earthquake in March 1964 is that data and records of conditions that existed prior to the earthquake are too sparse for a before-and-after comparison. It is hoped, however, that some extensive coring operations will be possible soon in northern waters, particularly near the Aleutians and off the coast of the Alaskan peninsula. These corings will be aimed primarily at discovering any recent transport of shallow water materials toward the great ocean depths—as, for example, the mechanism of nearby turbidity currents (undersea landslides).

Meanwhile, the greatest oceanographic mystery, apparently related geologically to the Alaskan disturbance, was the seiche (pronounced "saish") that caused waves 5 to 6 feet above normal to lash the northern coast of the Gulf of Mexico. The U.S. Coast and Geodetic Survey is still gathering records to define both the sequence and the mechanism of these widely scattered events. The Survey does not define it a seismic sea wave or tsunami, but it seems to qualify as one. Efforts are being made to assemble all available atmospheric pressure readings in the great Gulf area as a means of ascertaining that the seiche was not caused by differential barometric pressure, which would make its timing simply a matter of coincidence.

However, the timing of the first sea wave arrival on Gulf coast tide gauges ties in fairly well with the expected time of arrival from the first shock in Alaska; another disturbance of the Gulf sea level about 2½ hours later also coincides with the wave travel time from one of the strong aftershocks.

Produced Through Resonance

Another aspect of the Gulf seiches has been advanced in a recent issue of *Science*. According to Dr. William L. Dohn, of Columbia University's Lamont Geological Observatory, the 6-foot waves were produced through resonance with seismic waves that had traveled thousands of miles through the ground from Alaska; that is, the unusual Gulf coast waves could not have been caused by the great Pacific sea wave that was produced directly by the earth tremors on March 27. The water waves in the Gulf arrived at the same time as the seismic sea waves and were presumably created in resonance with the original seismic shocks.

Earthquakes combined with the sea make double trouble for man. Unrest begins when faults or deep fractures in the earth's crust, usually deep under the ocean, begin to vibrate as one mass slips against another. These massive shocks cause damage not only through the initial violent jolts but also through seismic sea waves or tsunamis. These expansive waves, traveling in all directions like the ripples caused by a stone dropped in a millpond, can reach undersea speeds of more than 600 miles an hour. Such waves are not high on the open ocean, in fact they can scarcely be noticed at all, but they pile up quickly at continental shelves or upon beaches, where they may suddenly rise to 90 feet or more with disastrous results.

The Aleutian earthquake of 1946 produced 55-foot high waves on the unwarned shores of the Hawaiian Islands, where some 150 lives were lost and hundreds of homes, cars, and livestock were destroyed. Now thanks to a seismic wave warning system for the Pacific, accurate predictions of the arrivals of such calamities prevent loss of life and permit advance salvage of much property. Today a far-off undersea 'quake in the Aleutians, or the Kuriles, or off the coast of Chile, or anywhere else in the vast tremor-ridden Pacific basin, will trigger alarms in the Hawaiian Islands, the West Coast of North America, the Fiji Islands, New Zealand, and every other nation, island, and territory tied in with the warning system.

Islands That Rise and Sink

A volcano is another force that continually changes sea geography, bringing volcanic islands into being and sometimes sinking them again. There have been several of these jack-in-a-box islands in the Pacific. A few years ago a new island popped out of the Azores as a pleasure cruise vessel sailed by, permitting its birth to be recorded on color film.

The most dramatic and disastrous case of such submarine volcanoes, under observation during the process of construction, was at Miojin Sho, off the Japanese islands. As Harris B. Stewart, Jr., describes it in *The Global Sea*: "The holocaust is well documented, but the price was high, for the entire scientific party and the crew of the Japanese research vessel *Kaijo Maru* were lost when the ship was completely destroyed by a sudden eruption directly beneath it."

Surtsey, the newest volcano island, began life on November 14, 1963, with the boiling of the sea 10 miles southwest of Westman Island, Iceland. It is named after the mythological Icelandic god Surter, a giant alleged to live within the earth who, among other things, is said to produce volcanoes and start hot springs flowing.

Surtsey's sudden volcanic activity began on the ocean floor some 120 meters below. Within two days an island had been formed nearly 1 kilometer long and 125 meters above sea level. Due to the nature of the formation, Surtsey began life as a sterile piece of land; the same is true of the ocean floor around its base.

Scientists consider Surtsey as an excellent prospect for a project in biogenesis. Duke University has proposed a close study of the development of life forms and ecologies on and around the newly formed island, including the reintroduction and spread of both floral and faunal life on the island, on its undersea slopes and on the nearby ocean floor. Air observations, for instance, show that at one point seagulls tried to settle Surtsey. By now, a number of life species have been found beginning to live there. The island is much larger and has attained a height of 170 meters, or about 550 feet. If it halts here and cools off, bird life should come back. Original support by Duke is being joined by the Office of Naval Research, the National Science Foundation, NASA, and others.

Deepest Depth

What is the greatest depth for all of the world's oceans? The H.M.S. *Cook*, exploring a vast undersea canyon east of the Philippines with echo-sounding equipment, hit bottom at 37,782 feet on November 6, 1962, the British Admiralty claims. The depth is 1,500 feet deeper than the previous record depth, reported in 1959 by the Soviet research ship *Vityaz* in the Pacific Ocean's Mariana Trench. The *Cook* depth lies in the Philippine Trench, one of several steep-walled furrows that gash the Pacific sea floor. Here is a world of total darkness, near-freezing temperatures, and pressures as high as 900 tons per square foot. A fraction of that pressure would be enough to crush a block of wood to half size.

Incredible as it may seem, however, life not only exists but thrives at these depths. Although probably barren of plant life, which requires light, such canyon floors support bacteria, sea anemones, mollusks, and minute crustaceans. Giant, deep-sea squids may also live there, sustaining themselves on food that floats down. The deepest descent by man was in the Navy's bathyscaph, a dive of 35,800 feet in the Mariana Trench off Guam.

Longest Mountain

All these trenches and huge undersea mountain ranges have opened vast new fields and research in the floor of the deep sea, which formerly was considered a monotonous plain. Soundings and corings during and since World War II reveal that the undersea landscape is extremely rugged. Most exciting of all was the discovery of the mid-Atlantic Ridge—a part of the longest mountain range in the world. This mighty system runs from the Arctic down through the North and South Atlantic to Antarctic seas, where it branches eastward to the Indian Ocean, and westward south of Australia, northwest to the central Pacific, and northward off the west coast of South America. This enormous underwater mountain range is also the site of many violent disturbances of the earth's crust, including earthquakes and volcanic activity.

During the spring of 1964, on an oceanographic cruise for the U.S. Coast and Geodetic Survey in the Pacific and Indian oceans, the *R/V Pioneer* indicated how much remains to be known about the sea floor. Within six months, the *R/V Pioneer* discovered several previously unknown undersea mountains, explored by echo soundings two giant submarine canyons off Ceylon—"both larger than the Grand Canyon"—and sent scuba divers down to search for the shallow top of another undersea mountain, taking thousands of color photographs of the bottom of the tropical sea.

Most outstanding discovery of the *Pioneer* cruise was "the world's steepest continental slope," found where Ceylon drops down into the Bay of Bengal. Whereas the pitch of the average continental slope ranges between 4 and 15 degrees, this subsea incline exceeded 45 degrees—falling from a depth of 180 feet to 12,000 feet in less than 18 miles. Expedition chief scientist Dr. Harris B. Stewart reports that the steepest part of the slope is located about 20 miles south of Trincomalee and is about 2 miles long.

Abyssal Plains and Guyots

In many other ways the underseas landscape is amazingly varied. Although scientists once considered most of the bottom monotonously flat, terming it "the abyssal plains," recent study indicates it is quite lumpy, with ups and downs that average 1,200 feet. This rough domain covers about half of the ocean floor, an area equal to that of all exposed land on earth. Yet actually little is known about its origin, composition, and topography. Even its largest hills remain too small to be studied by the seismic refraction techniques generally used, and many of them are so steep that scientists find difficulty in determining their shape by echo-sounders. Until recently, an individual hill could rarely if ever be revisited, since navigation techniques were too slow and not precise enough.

Now, taut wire buoys are relatively simple to install, and bottom-sampling devices can be more reliably located on selected parts of the sea floor. A research grant received by the Institute of Marine Science, University of Miami, to continue this study, will enable scientists to obtain more landmarks in the vast unknown wastes of the sea.

Occasionally the abyssal plains are dotted by sizeable peaks or sea mounts. Most unusual of these isolated structures are the guyots. With the shape of a truncated cone, guyots have tops as flat as a football field and lie several hundred fathoms under the sea. Scientists believe their tops were levelled off by waves when the peaks were at sea level. Did a rise in sea level, or a depression of the sea floor, then "drown" these restless peaks under the ocean?

Additional study of the sea may determine the answer, as well as to the kindred problem of the reef-building corals of tropic waters. Dormant or extinct volcanoes have often provided platforms for the growth of coral reefs, which continue to grow when the sea level rises or when peaks subside. When the islands sink too deep for coral activity, do the peaks become submerged as sea mounts or guyots?

Here, again, is the old question: originally did the sea rise or did the peaks subside, and how and why? Since Darwin, this has been one of the lively controversies of modern science, and the debate goes on—a challenge for present and perhaps future generations.

CHAPTER VI

MOST PRECIOUS MINERAL—AND OTHERS

ASK THE AVERAGE PERSON: "What is the most precious substance in the world?" and likely the reply will be gold, or platinum, or diamonds, or maybe pearls (the only gem to originate in the sea). But the correct answer is fresh water!

To put it another way, fresh water ranks first because man cannot live without it. Most of us, if we give the subject any thought at all, consider fresh water, evaporated by the sun from the sea, as unlimited.

Water Never Disappears

Technically, this should be so. The clouds are still dropping the same amount of rainfall as ever. Basic water never disappears. Even sea level variations have been very minor over the centuries known to man. The oceans cover nearly three quarters of the earth and shall continue to do so, no matter how the cycle of evaporation and rainfall is abused by man's comsumption and pollution of water.

Major droughts occur on land, due to shifting winds and temperatures, but the same amount of rain, on an average, falls from the sky, and the same amount is returned to the sea.

Why, then, is there a very real fresh water shortage today in regions that only a few years ago had abundant supplies for man, beast, farm, and factory, and still receive the same rainfall? There are several reasons why the need and uses of potable water have skyrocketed. First and foremost is the world's current population explosion, dating from the end of World War II and accelerating at an amazing rate. From it comes enormously stepped-up demands for more fresh water in processing all kinds of industrial products, and in agriculture, forestry, and recreation. Overuse of the soil and forests resulting in rapid runoff, and wastes from factories, homes, and farm pesticides restrict the availability of many streams, lakes, and rivers once abundant with fresh water.

Some Can Be Retrieved

Some of the pollutants can be removed, and potable water be retrieved. Some supplies of fresh water can still be pumped from large natural underground reservoirs, but many of these, particularly in the Plains States, are brackish. Man himself is a great indulger. Our personal water uses may seem small, but in aggregate in this plumbing era they are enormous. The average man, for instance, consumes about a ton of water a year. Just flushing a toilet requires 4 to 5 gallons, and a tub or a shower twice as much. Vegetables and meat draw upon about 1,000 pounds of fresh water to produce 1 pound of food; to produce a ton of steel requires several thousand gallons of water.

Faced with such a multitude of shortages, old and new, it is not very comforting to learn further that, of the world's total water supply, no more than 3 per cent is fresh water, and, of this, about 80 per cent is already locked up in ice and snow, mostly in the polar ice caps. Even if portions of the icecaps could be melted by new technical devices, the water resulting from it would be too far away to be supplied at a reasonable price.

Bahama Reefs — undersea world. (John Storr)

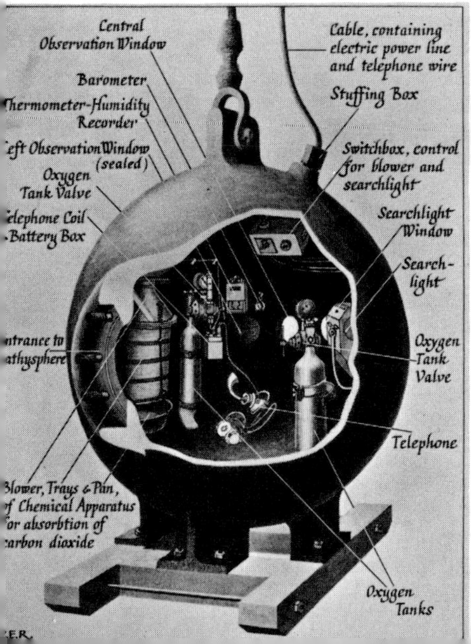
Central Observation Window
Barometer
Thermometer-Humidity Recorder
Left Observation Window (sealed)
Oxygen Tank Valve
Telephone Coil Battery Box
Entrance to Bathysphere
Blower, Trays & Pan, of Chemical Apparatus for absorbtion of carbon dioxide
Cable, containing electric power line and telephone wire
Stuffing Box
Switchbox, control for blower and searchlight
Searchlight Window
Search-light
Oxygen Tank Valve
Telephone
Oxygen Tanks

Cut-away drawing of the Bathysphere used during the William Beebe Expedition off Bermuda in 1934 — the earliest of man's invasion of the sea's depths. (National Geographic Society)

International Ice Patrol—a half-a-century operation run by the U.S. Coast Guard. (U.S. Coast Guard)

The third U.S. government saline water pilot plant, San Diego, California. (Department of the Interior)

Sun evaporation basins for sea water, Bahamas — the oldest process for obtaining minerals from the sea. (Bahama News)

U.S. Navy carrier in a "washdown" system to dispose of radioactive contamination. The jets near the bow let off colored steam to stimulate atomic fallout. (U.S. Navy)

A scientist checks on an unmanned weather station, called *Nomad*, at sea. (U.S. Navy)

Primitive fisheries of India—catch is emptied aboard a trawler where it will be washed and sorted. (Food and Agriculture Organization)

Dredging soft-shell or long-nose clams in Chesapeake Bay, St. Michaels, Maryland. (Fletcher Hanks)

R/V Flip — Floating Instrument Platform — in operation in the North Pacific is used for sensitive oceanographic measurements at sea.

A "Texas Tower" used exclusively for oceanographic research, off San Diego, California. (U.S. Navy)

"Mesocaph" interior — tourist submarine used on Lake Geneva, Switzerland. (Pfister Zurich)

"Mesocaph" exterior, Auguste Piccard. (Actualités Suisses Lausanne)

Artist's sketch shows how man could explore "inner space" and tap the vast natural resources by nuclear reactor (left) to support an undersea community. (Westinghouse Photo)

This predicted automated ocean convoy for overseas transportation of bulk cargoes may be a reality soon. (Roy Grinnell, The Martin Co.)

Largest oceanographic land base, Woods Hole, Massachusetts. (Woods Hole Oceanographic Institute)

Printed in U.S.A.

MOST PRECIOUS MINERAL—AND OTHERS • 113

Turn to the Sea Itself

Actually only two practical solutions meet the fresh water situation today. One is better use of water we now have by erecting more dams to prevent useless run off and by purifying polluted streams, even to the point of reclaiming waste sewage water. Some of these methods are being used very effectively, but experts say they won't take care of future water consumption, especially in great suburban areas, such as those along the Atlantic seaboard and in southern California.

This brings us to the only other possibility—man must turn to the limitless sea itself, accelerating Nature's method of creating fresh water through saline water methods. This is not a brand new idea. Boiling seawater and then condensing steam into fresh water has been done on ships for many years. But this method is expensive for large-quantity use, and it leaves heavy scale and corrosion that require costly overhauls.

Meanwhile, scientists have found several different ways of de-salting seawater without boiling it and leaving expensive scale. But which method would be best to use in big quantities, and at what cost, remains to be settled. However, considerable progress in testing and experimenting has been moving along at an encouraging rate.

In fact, numerous processes for making potable water corner of the globe. Many of these processes are technifrom saline water have been offered from almost every nically sound, but some are economically less attractive than others. Virtually all of these processes have been under extensive study in this country, by both private and govermental organizations. Costly experiments of this vast nature do not appeal to private enterprise, although economists recognize that the need for more fresh water, from any possible source, is urgent.

The federal government finally agreed to set up an Office of Saline Water under the Department of the Interior to develop several "demonstration processes" which showed promise, in tests, of cheap and easy output of fresh water in quantities. The government agreed that if and when they prove to be operating satisfactorily, these plants and their blueprints for duplication would be turned over to private corporations or municipalities. To prevent favoring only seaboard enterprises, at least two types of demonstration plants were set up near the huge brackish underground reservoirs of the Middle West and the Southwest.

Extra Dividends

The Office of Saline Water was directed to watch for and list numerous mineral residues—such as potash, magnesium, iodine, bromine, and scores of minor compounds—which might become extra dividends. As a Texan expert (C. M. Shigley, of Freeport) declared: "The large scale recoveries of bromine and magnesium . . . are indicative of a pronounced trend toward using the seas for more of life's needs. It is natural that this should be. The seas, bordering every continent, represent a global source of supply. They are practicably inexhaustible. Total quantities of available salts reach astronomical figures and are unquestionably increasing with the daily contribution of the rivers, while other mineral resources are being depleted." A prophetic observation!

"Referred to Committee"

The government's first saline water conversion bill was introduced before Congress in 1948 and again in 1949. But legislation did not progress beyond the routine "referred to committee" stage. President Truman gave it a boost in his budget message of 1950. It was not until 1958, however, that the Department of the Interior was authorized to "construct and operate not less than five saline water conversion plants to demonstrate the reliability, engineering, operating and economic potentials of the most promising sea or brackish water conversion processes."

Action came rapidly soon after that. On May 31, 1961, President Kennedy pushed a special button on his desk in the White House, signalling the start-up, at Freeport, Texas, of the first saline water conversion demonstration unit. How has this unique government agency (OSW) so quickly moved into operation with little friction or fanfare? Perhaps one answer is proper planning. All the research work involved was conducted by contract with other existing federal agencies and with universities, private research organizations, and industrial firms. Using this technique, the Office of Saline Water utilized some of the nation's finest scientists and specialists in many fields—physics, chemistry, biology, and the earth sciences, plus engineering, social sciences, and economics—and thus avoided a costly rigid organization.

Two Types of Energy Used

Briefly, the new saline processes consume energy, either in the form of electric power or other heat sources. At the present state of technology, electrically driven processes are more adaptable to brackish water than to seawater, or rather have been demonstrated only in comparatively smaller supplies. Technology of these electrical processes is still developing, and some offer a potential of producing low-cost fresh water from seawater for large water supplies.

Following the enactment of the demonstration-plant legislation, several cities were selected to process fresh water capacities from sea and brackish waters. They are as follows:

Area	Location	Process	Capacity
Gulf Coast	Freeport, Texas	Long-tube vertical multi-effect distillation	1,000,000 gallons per day
West Coast	San Diego, California	Multistage flash distillation	1,000,000 gallons per day
Northern Great Plains	Webster, South Dakota	Electrodialysis (membrane process)	250,000 gallons per day
Air Areas of Southwest	Roswell, New Mexico	Forced-circulation vapor-compression	1,000,000 gallons per day
East Coast	Wrightsville Beach, North Carolina	Freezing (near completion)	1,000,000 gallons per day

Much valuable information will be obtained from the construction and operation of these first plants, built by the Department of the Interior. Prior to their erection, the most efficient conversion plants in operation were producing fresh water at costs ranging *upward* of $1.75 per thousand gallons, some as high as $7.00 per thousand gallons. Seawater conversion in the demonstration plants has been reduced to $1.00 to $1.25 per thousand gallons, and inland brackish water is being desalted for less than $1.00 per thousand gallons. This is still high compared with the cost of 15¢ to 75¢ per thousand gallons to distribute and purify domestic fresh water from streams, lakes, and springs. Experts expect, however by building larger plants run with a cheap source of power (nuclear energy) to desalt seawater from 10 to 25 million gallons a day and to achieve a figure of 25¢ to 30¢ per thousand gallons. Desalted seawater cheap enough for irrigation (1¢ to 5¢ per thousand gallons) is still not in sight.

Fringe Methods

In addition to the major demonstration plants, fringe methods, related to many new or improved former suggestions, are being explored. Pilot plants are an important phase of various applied research programs of the Office of Saline Water, bridging the gap between laboratories on the one hand and demonstration or commerical producing plants on the other. The size of a pilot plant is determined by the technical needs of the moment; it may vary from such small operations as 1,000 gallons per day to 50,000 gallons per day.

One of the most unusual of the pilot projects today is testing a process known as reverse osmosis, at San Diego, California. When pure water and a salt solution are placed on opposite sides of a semipermeable membrane (ideally, permeable to salt), fresh water will flow through the membrane and dilute the salt solution. This is the well-known process of osmosis. If fresh water flow is prevented, a hydrostatic pressure, known as the osmotic pressure, builds up in the salt solution in proportion to the concentration of salt.

Under these conditions, an application of hydrostatic pressure to the salt solution, in excess of the osmotic pressure, will generate a flow of fresh water from the salt solution, through the membrane, to the fresh water side. This process, known as reverse osmosis, provides an unique technique for desalinization. Its feasibility has been demonstrated on a pilot-plant scale; it is simple to operate and its energy requirements may approach the theoretical minimum as closely as any process. But, according to a report of an Interagency Task Group of the Office of Science and Technology, Executive Office of the President, further development and plant operating experience will be required before reverse osmosis can be considered as a major desalinization process for the future.

Put the Sun to Work

An even simpler saline water conversion process uses solar energy. It requires no moving parts, nor any fuel. It is just the opposite of the great salt pans in some arid regions, which evaporate all water, leaving a residue of salts desired. This experimental greenhouse-type-still uses a shallow basin, painted black to absorb the sun's heat. When the basin is filled with saline water, the heat of the sun causes the water to evaporate. As the vapor rises it contacts a cooler glass or plastic film surface above the basin, where it condenses or runs down into collecting troughs on each side of the still.

In this type of still, under good sunshine conditions, approximately one pound of fresh water per day per square foot of surface can be obtained. This is no gusher, of course, but the method may be useful in arid areas rich in sunshine, relatively poor in other fuels, and remote from all other fresh water sources.

Meanwhile, saline water conversion may soon take an enormous step. A proposed program for large-scale nuclear power, combined with desalinization plants, was released recently (1964) by the White House Office of Science and Technology. This brilliant study, which began early in 1963, was prepared under the direction of Dr. Roger Revelle, former director of Scripps Institution of Oceanography. Combined installations producing 1,300 to 1,900 megawatts of marketable electric energy and 500 to 800 million gallons of water a day are expected to be feasible by 1975. Electric power, valued at 2.3 to 2.5 mills per kilowatt-hour, would cost only 20¢ to 25¢ per 1,000 gallons at the plant site. The report states that 240-megawatt, 220-million-gallons-per-day plants could be built using present techniques.

Next Steps Needed

Further research and operation recommended in the report are:

(a) Development and construction of a distillation unit with a capacity of about 10 million gallons per day. The largest unit now in operation in the United States is a 1.4 million-gallon unit.
(b) Planning and feasibility studies on a combined reactor desalinization and electric power plant of the range of 200 megawatts and 50 million gallons of water a day. The Interior Department and the Atomic Energy Commission would do the work.
(c) Continued research and development on desalinization methods other than distillation, for possible use in the combined concept.
(d) Possible plant site studies by Interior and the AEC.
(e) Specification by the AEC of the reactor types most suitable for development in sizes of around 8,000 thermal megawatts, under alternative methods of financing.

Active in "Cold War"

Saline water conversion has also taken an active part in the "cold war." When the supply of fresh water at the U.S. Naval Base in Guantanamo was cut off by the Cubans, the demonstration plant at "Point Loma I" was quickly dismantled and shipped from San Diego to the base at Guantanamo. It has been replaced at San Diego by "Point Loma II," a similar but larger multistage, multi-effect flash distillation plant, which eventually may be stepped up from the former production of 1 million gallons of fresh water a day to 1.5 million gallons daily.

For many years the Florida Keys have had an acute fresh water problem. During World War II, the Navy ran a 140-mile fresh water pipeline from the Florida mainland to Key West. However, it is expensive to maintain and subject to breaks during hurricanes. Sometimes a wayward bus or truck runs off the Key highway, which parallels the pipeline, and breaks the vital artery. Plans are now being considered to give the lower Keys, near Key West, a combination thermal-electric and seawater desalting plant, the first large-scale plant of its kind. The Atomic Energy Commission is proceeding with studies on the utilization of nuclear power as a source of heat for the combination plant.

Descaling Chain-Reaction

Scale-forming substances, which ordinarily tend to gather on desalting equipment, cause loss of efficiency. To offset scale, a pilot plant is being erected at the Office of Saline Water Research and Development Test Station at Wrightsville Beach, North Carolina. Since the rate of scale formation increases with temperature rise, low distillation temperatures must be used. However, higher temperatures would improve both efficiencies and capacities. Hence a chemical process is being used to descale seawater. These chemicals will eliminate acids now used for partial control of scale formation and thus effect economies through the use of less expensive construction materials.

At the same time, the plant is expected to produce highly concentrated brines, which might make recovering of by-products from brines economically feasible. This in turn should shift some of the cost of producing descaled water from the sea to the by-products, and thus reduce the net cost of the descaled water.

Supermarket for All

Because saline water conversion has become the bright new jewel in the sea's vast resources, we should not overlook, however, the other fabulous minerals which can be derived directly or indirectly from the sea. The ocean's dowry is actually a gigantic supermarket for all who will explore and exploit it. Beyond the confines of coastal limits, seawater and the sea bottom are theoretically free to all. In recent years, however, 3-mile limit marking extent of ownership by adjacent land has been extended far over and into the sea by certain nations—without any legal right to do so—to enlarge their own grandiose ambitions.

An international compact is urgently needed to settle several already heated disputes on what has been considered "the high seas," economically available to everyone in peacetime. Unless an agreement of international sea rights can soon be properly reestablished or adjusted, more trouble concerning such matters as fisheries, oil, metals, and other resources along the rich continental shelves and in even deeper waters, are likely to arise to plague us all.

Heavier than Water Itself

The value of seawater itself cannot be overemphasized. Incredible as it may seem, seawater contains traces of all the important elements known to man, including certain minerals that are many times heavier than water itself. Most minerals, of course, are not present in their native state, even when they are too tiny to be seen by the naked eye. But they do exist, in even the clearest glass of seawater, as hundreds of variations of dissolved compounds or salts.

For instance, a cubic mile of seawater contains 18 million tons of magnesium, that most versatile light-weight metal of which the sea is almost the only source, 25 tons of gold, and huge quantities of other chemical compounds, such as calcium, sulfur, sodium, chlorine, potassium, bromine, and iodine, the latter two derived only from the sea. It also holds dissolved salts of silver, aluminum, iron, nickel, chromium, radium, and even that rising star of the atomic age—uranium.

But don't invest any money on the constantly recurring reports that "the sea is loaded with gold." They are true if you are talking about the oceans of the world as a whole. But gold is in such minute particles in the sea as to make extraction unprofitable, although repeated efforts have been made. A classic unsuccessful example was the German *Meteor* expedition to the mid-Atlantic in 1927, with the objective of obtaining enough gold from the sea to pay the German war debt.

Salt a Safer Bet

A very much safer bet would be common salt,—next to fresh water itself, the most important and valuable mineral in the world. The average person requires from 16 to 17 pounds of it a year. In addition, salt is still the most effective preservative of food. While all salt (sodium chloride) has been derived from the sea, or from salt beds or salt lakes that are residues of former seas, most of the world's needs today—an estimated 5 million tons a year—are easily met by land deposits. But the sea could meet the demand easily if other sources were exhausted. To return to our cubic mile of sea water, it contains enough salt to supply the world's needs for nine years. The ocean as a whole contains enough salt for 2½ million years, even if it were not continually replenished.

Not only is common or table salt the easiest dissolved mineral to obtain from the ocean, it is also the earliest sea chemical known to man. The Chinese mentioned salt from the sea in 2200 B.C. The Greek philosopher Aristotle described a method of desalting sea water in his *Meteorologia*, and praises the merits of ordinary sea salt, whose variety of trace elements, beneficial to health, have only been rediscovered during modern medicine's quest of "a balanced diet." Solar evaporation of salt, a simple process, is still in use in many parts of the world, notably in Japan, the Near East, India, the southern Bahamas, and Puerto Rico.

"Mineral Mines" Loaded

Aside from common salt and other compounds of salts, the sea's mineral mines are loaded with hundreds of other valuables, including solid metals, crystals, fluids, and gases. Perhaps the most remarkable of all are nodules, which are not chips from larger pieces of metal but units that have accumulated from seawater, beginning with bits of sand, sharks teeth, or other tiny objects. The most abundant pure metal in these nodules is manganese, an extremely valuable element used in strengthening steel, but the nodules also contain other metals, such as copper, nickel and cobalt. Blanketing some parts of the sea floor, nodules still mystify scientists, who estimate that there are 1.5 trillion tons of nodules under the Pacific alone. Some of them are as large as golf balls and, as the supply of them increases constantly, they should be a replenishing source of needed minerals, a self-renewing mine, forever.

The cost of mining them is a big deterrent. Although we obtain scarce manganese only from Brazil and India, it is not yet valuable enough to extract it profitably from the sea bottom. Equipment needed for this type of deep-sea mining will include a dredge with suction pipes capable of picking up the nodules from the sea bottom, like a vacuum sweeper. Because the operation would take place in water too deep for man's participation, undersea TV cameras would be needed to monitor the machinery.

Engineers predict that certain metals in these sea-floor nodules will eventually be extracted at a cost of only 50 to 75 per cent of the expense of obtaining them from land deposits today. Manganese, not yet valuable enough in itself to pay for the work, might bring up with it other such desirable elements as nickel, cobalt, molybdenum, and zirconium. If the operators were especially lucky, they might also gather up some meteorites, which have showered into the sea from space for eons. As museum specimens, these would have more value than the minerals they contain.

Anyone's Best Friend

As time goes on, more and more materials are being found on the bottom of the sea. Diamonds have recently joined the parade. Existence of diamond deposits under the Atlantic off the coast of Africa has been suspected for some time. In the early 1960s a promising new source of diamonds was discovered in an offshore area of South-West Africa. An American named Samuel Collins, since 1962, has extracted more than 1.5 million dollars worth of gemstones from the Chamais Bay area north of the Orange River.

Two theories on the source of the South-West African diamonds have been advanced. One holds that the stones were swept by currents from volcanic sources under the sea; the second belief is that the gems originated inland and were carried to the coast and beyond by ancient rivers.

The search for underwater diamonds is based on the world's only floating minehead. Diamond-bearing sand and gravel are loosened from the ocean floor by jets of compressed air, then sucked up to a barge through a pipeline. On the barge, the sand and gravel are combed for diamonds, and all but the gems are thrown overboard. Each ton of sand and gravel from the ocean beds yields an average of one diamond. The Marine Diamond Corporation reported during July of 1963 the recovery of about 700 carats of gemstone, mostly small, per day—but not every day. Fog, storms and huge waves crash against the barge frequently. The miners, who have nowhere to go for recreation, become bored, tired, and often seasick.

Oil From the Sea

Early in the 1920s, American industry began pumping oil from beneath the ocean, the first wells being sunk in shallow waters off the northern coast of South America. These were followed by deeper wells along the southern and western coastlines of the United States. Similar operations have been extended in many parts of the world.

It is not an easy task to obtain oil, gas, and sulfur from the sea. Cost of equipment, drilling, and operations, say for a 10,000-foot well, is about 50 per cent more offshore than onshore. However, offshore drilling to date has been more productive (about 4 to 1) in terms of reserves found. The magnitude of the offshore operations may be illustrated by figures for the Louisiana marine area. Total investment at the end of 1962 exceeded $3 billion, with a forecast of $2.6 billion to be invested in the next five years. While earnings thus far do not quite meet the industry's expenditures, its willingness to invest in offshore operations testifies to its faith in the future.

The oil industry, according to the Interagency Committee on Oceanography, has been relatively self-reliant in its oceanography and underwater geology. Information in its files on the topography and structure of many areas along the continental shelf probably exceeds that available elsewhere in both scientific quality and quantity. The beneficial effect of permanent structures, sometimes called "Texas Towers," on fishing is well known. These structures attract fish and provide a desirable environment for them. Underwater television cameras used by the industry already have photographed forms of sea life not known before.

Much Geological Data

Technically, many of the innovations developed in the search for oil under the sea have been immediately useful to other industries and other scientific pursuits. Much geological data, now unavailable for proprietary reasons, would also be of great general value if and when the oil industry releases it in the future. Exploration of marine areas by the oil industry has been largely confined to profitable areas, as for example along the Gulf Coast and the coast of California where producing fields and geologic conditions of promise extend seaward. As on land, the industry looks to government for exploration in areas of unknown or marginal oil and gas potential.

Increasing attention is being paid to the geochemistry of sediments and analysis of the "interstitial" (space between) water squeezed from deep-sea cores. The relationship between components of biological origin and the physical environment is being examined in cores taken from the Yucatan basin. Interstitial water from cores taken off Cape Cod has been found to have higher acidity than the bottom water of the area, probably because of high carbon dioxide pressures developed by bacterial decomposition in the sediments.

Frontier of the Chemist

What is the future along the chemical frontiers of the sea? Prospects are excellent, although major development was slow until recently. Crude soda and potash were obtained from the ashes of seaweed in Scotland in 1720, and iodine (also from seaweed) and magnesia were recovered in Europe in the 19th century. But not much attention was paid to the ocean as a mineral and chemical source until 1923, when magnesium and gypsum were produced from bitterns (mother liquor in salt-works after the salt has crystallized out) drawn from San Francisco Bay. A short while later, the first seawater bromine was recovered on a commercial scale from the bitterns of the same plant, and industry began to take notice of the oceans as something more than a means of travel.

It was the sharp increase in the use of antiknock gasoline, in 1933, that really put the sea in big mineral business. Previously plants, drawing upon subterranean brines, were the only source of bromine used in ethylene dibromide, a necessary associate of tetraethyl lead in the making of quiet motor fuel. In 1940, further demands for bromine, extracted directly from seawater without prior concentration of sea salts, led to the erection of a major plant at Freeport, Texas. There, in 1941, a nearby unit produced the first magnesium metal from Gulf water, eliminating the intermediate process of obtaining magnesium chloride from bitterns.

Uses of "Middlemen"

Still another important seawater mineral is calcium. Here a "middleman" helps us. Shellfish constantly extract calcium from the sea and make it available to man in their shells or in limestone (calcium carbonate) of old shell beds. This is a centuries-old worldwide chemical process which makes the efforts of man seem puny in comparison. Processes for extraction exist for some elements which appear scarcely as a trace in chemical analysis of the water. Cell tissues of certain marine plants and animals have become highly efficient in concentrating rare compounds, such as the iodine salts found in seaweeds.

When we can learn this trick of direct extractions from the water, according to *Sea Frontiers*, of the International Oceanographic Foundation, we shall be nearer economic success in extensive mining of the oceans. One of the surprising discoveries in the field was that the small, soft-bodied sea squirts, or tunicates, can extract vanadium from salt water, yet chemists are unable to find this trace element by laboratory analysis of the water itself—until the sea squirt has done his job. From the same thin sea-solution other shellfish and seaweeds have been able also to concentrate such elements as copper, cobalt, and silica.

Mining the vast resources of the sea for our economic welfare is not just a paper scheme, nor is it a nebulous hope. On a modest but growing scale, it is an actuality. In place of the mechanical engineer with his steam shovel, or the miner with his pick and shovel, "maritime mining" is still largely the frontier of the chemist. Hope for extraction of valuable minerals on a large commercial scale hangs upon the results of recently expanded research in this new field, and particularly the development of promising methods of handling extremely dilute solutions, such as those involving ion-exchange techniques.

The future development of the ocean's resources, like the opening of any new land, will require the patient effort of many people, plus daring financing, and a coupling of scientific research with practical know-how.

CHAPTER VII

POISONING THE SEA

BECAUSE THE SEA has been the largest, deepest, and most secretive place on earth, it has been considered, for centuries, the safest place to dump anything unwanted. Then came the atomic age, with fallout, and radioactive waste materials. Man soon learned that it is not a good idea to dump *all* things into the ocean, and particularly not unlimited radioactive waste products. Other pollution of the sea, such as garbage, human wastes from contaminated rivers, old trash, and junk, either quickly disappears or becomes part of the bottom. But radiation properties cannot be destroyed by any immediate reversal of the method whereby they were originally produced, and the sea has a way of returning radioactive things.

It is difficult for anyone except experts in radioactive matters to determine just where nuclear reactions are injurious to man, sea creatures, or inanimate things. Radioactive wastes exist in a wide range of values. According to the hearings on "Industrial Radioactive Waste Disposal," Joint Committee on Atomic Energy (Congress of the United States, 1959), high-level wastes have been defined as those with "concentrations of hundreds of thousands of curie per gallon," while low-level wastes are those with "concentrations in the range of one microcurie per gallon." "Curie" is a measure of the activity of a radioisotope and is approximately the rate of disintegration of one gram of radium; "microcurie" is one-millionth of this value.

Two Main Approaches

The tremendous range in the degree of radioactivity has forced two main approaches to the waste-disposal problem: (1) the radioactive high-level wastes, the ones more dangerous to man and (2) the low-level and less dangerous wastes, which can be diluted and easily dispersed. Only the latter are now being consigned to the sea. In fact, there has been very little disposal of radioactive materials at sea since 1960, when land burial sites were made available for commercial wastes. At present all high-level and even intermediate-level wastes are contained in storage tanks on land.

Here, too, much low-level waste is contained until it can be treated and then discharged into rivers or through long pipes into the sea. Or it may still be sealed in concrete containers and disposed of at sea, the original method of dumping such materials.

Actually, how far we should go in using what and how much of any nuclear dispersal at sea is still not known. Our knowledge of the scales or actual rates of curies and their diffusion is still slight, especially concerning the movements of the wastes from one part of the ocean to another. The amount of absorption of nuclear poison that will be taken up by individual molecules, and the path they take through the waters, animals, and sediments of the sea are also largely unknown, although some of this information is gradually becoming available to scientists. Even a slight deviation from normal oceanic conditions, we know, can cause regional disaster, as is the case with the "red tide" in the Gulf of Mexico, or the El Niño off Peru, where fishes are killed by the thousands by other disturbed conditions. The same could possibly be done with nuclear wastes, unless we are careful of the quantity and places we use them.

For some time the U.S. Atomic Energy Commission has been supporting basic research in the fields of oceanic circulation, uptake of elements by organisms, ion exchange between seawater and the ocean floor sediments, and other research projects which might produce data that will be of use in evaluating the sea as a disposal site for radioactive unwanted products.

Fallout Prime Danger

Not all the atomic wastes introduced into the sea in recent years were put there by man disposing of containers of leftover material from power plants, medical spoils, and other such sources. Fallout from nuclear weapons tests has been by far the principal man-made source of radioactive contamination. About 340 nuclear detonations in the atmosphere, by all nations testing, have been announced (1964). The total energy release has been about 511 million tons (MT) equivalent of TNT, with U.S.S.R. tests accounting for about 70 per cent of the total. Included in this total are about 193 million tons of energy released by fission—the process that creates the radioactive fission products present in fallout.

The signing of the Limited Test Ban Treaty, in September 1963, marked the close of 14 years of such testing over an 18-year period and brought to an end the major hazards—as long as the Treaty is observed. But the treaty does not, of course, mark the end of a need for further information and interpretation of data concerning the health aspects of all nuclear weapons testing, past and present. An enormous amount of information has already been assembled, far more than could be evaluated in a book of this type. But for those who wish to know more about the basic questions concerning the testing of nuclear weapons, an easily read booklet has been published by the U.S. Atomic Energy Commission: *Health Aspects of Nuclear Weapons Testing*, (U.S. Government Printing Office, Washington, D.C., 1964: OL-729-548. Price 25¢).

Planktonic Warfare

The need for more understanding of the use of nuclear weapons and atomic wastes at sea is more than academic. Military strategists warn us that enemy submarines could drop atomic wastes or concentrated raw atomic materials deliberately in the best fishing grounds, beginning a chain reaction of atomic poisoning from plankton to fish to man.

Another method of nuclear poisoning of the sea would be to plant by submarines some of the more deadly atomic reagents. These in turn may destroy the base of the food chain completely, and progressively decimate by starvation the larger fishes. Are there any reagents for this kind of planktonic warfare? Not as far as we know, but we can hope and try, and redouble our research.

Brighter Side to Atom

Why is it that when you mention nuclear or atomic energy to the average person he becomes apprehensive, anticipating something ugly or unfavorable? He instinctively begins to think in terms of big bombs, or safeguards with radiation-measuring badges or decontamination. Not too long ago, the atom was almost totally a fearsome thing, and its use in warfare and even in testing left poisons on both land and sea.

But today there is a brighter side to the atom that should be mentioned briefly here, too, so that we shall not give a lopsided picture. In fact, nuclear energy is playing a vital and useful role in the life of every man, woman, and child in the United States today. In the years ahead it will help increasingly all the peoples of the earth on land and at sea.

It all began with the existence of isotopes, discovered about 1913, after nearly a decade of experimenting with naturally radioactive materials. Certain isotopes are unstable and undergo a process of decay, during which they emit radiation. Such isotopes are called radioisotopes.

"Atom Smashers"

By the early 1930s scientists had learned that, by bombarding normally stable chemical elements with subatomic particles, using particle accelerators ("atom smashers"), radioactivity could be induced in the elements. That is, radioisotopes could be made artificially. Quantity production became feasible after the development of nuclear reactors during World War II. Radioisotopes differ in the types of radiation they emit and in the rate at which they decay, or lose their radioactivity. These characteristics help determine their usefulness as well as their dangers to man.

Because radioisotopes vary in the rates at which they decay, it has become customary to measure them in terms of the time required for half the unstable nuclei, in a pure sample, to decay. This time is called the radioisotope's "half life." Half-lives of different radioisotopes vary enormously. For example, nitrogen-12 has a half-life of only 12/1,000 second, while the half-life of iodine-129 is 16 million years, as we figure it today.

Chief Uses Today

So much for background, now what are the chief uses of radioisotopes today? There are four basically different uses: (1) Radioisotopes are used as fixed sources of radiation to make some change in a target material. For example, cancerous tissue may be destroyed by radiation therapy; male insects of some harmful variety may be sterilized by radiation to prevent reproduction; or food products may be irradiated to kill the bacteria which cause decay.

(2) Radioisotopes are also used as fixed sources of radiation, in measuring systems that provide information about a target by sensing the radiation which penetrates it or is reflected from it. Examples include systems for measuring the thickness of a moving sheet of metal, the liquid level in a closed container, and the density of the upper atmosphere.

(3) The most common way of using radioisotopes has developed from certain techniques in medical and agricultural research. Here small amounts of radioisotopes (tracers) are mixed directly into the material of interest. Then, by detecting their radiations with instruments such as Geiger counters, it is possible to follow, or trace, the material's course as it undergoes some physical, chemical, or biological process. Typical uses are in tracing the uptake of fertilizers by plants, tracing the absorption of iodine by the human thyroid gland, and tracing water flow to locate underground water supplies.

(4) Radioisotopes also provide the basis for power generators. Radiations from an appreciable amount of radioactive material sealed in a container are absorbed in the container, thereby generating heat. High-density sources of radiation can create high temperatures. The most familiar method is to use the heat to boil water; a more direct method is called thermoelectric conversion. In the latter, fuel decays spontaneously, emitting particles that produce heat upon absorption, thermocouples convert heat directly into electricity, and electricity is tapped from terminals to which thermocouples are connected.

Serve In Isolated Places

There are many out-of-the-way places on land and at sea where electrical power is needed for weather stations, navigational beacons, and other special installations. It is costly to provide man with fuel and the necessities of life in these remote locations. The development of cheap, reliable, long-lived radioisotope generators may help to solve this problem. Generators with no moving parts have an inherent reliability and freedom from maintenance. The slow decay of isotopes, such as strontium-90 and cesium-137, can provide years of operating life.

Perhaps the most unusual oceanographic development of radioisotopes is the undersea navigational beacon, or SNAP-7E. As part of a two-year testing program, the thermoelectric generator and other equipment are housed in an experimental device made to withstand tremendous pressure, and moored 15,000 feet below the surface of the Atlantic Ocean. It uses four capsules, containing 31,000 curies of strontium-90 titanate fuel. A navigator will use this beacon just as he uses a radio beacon or lighthouse. Knowing the position of the beacon on the chart, he can determine the position of his ship with an underwater listening device.

Radiation "Pasteurized"

On February 8, 1963, the Food and Drug Administration of the U.S. Department of Health, Education and Welfare ruled that bacon preserved by radiation is perfectly safe and fit for unlimited human consumption. With that ruling a new chapter began in man's age-long battle to preserve his food from spoilage. Except for canning, radiation processing is the only original method of preserving food devised by man since the dawn of history. Ionizing radiation preserves foods by inhibiting bacterial growth or by destroying bacteria and other microorganisms. The food has been radiation "pasteurized"—exposed to low but safe levels of nuclear radiation.

Oranges as sweet and juicy long after harvest as if just picked, strawberries firm and free of mold many miles and weeks away from harvest, bacon, ham, and chicken that have *not* been near a refrigerator are fed to hundreds of soldiers who find them the equal of normal fresh products—all because they have been exposed to levels of radiation high enough to kill bacteria.

Fish of Prime Interest

Most important of all to oceanographers is the potential market for irradiated fish, now being studied by cooperative programs of the Atomic Energy Commission, the Department of the Interior, and the Department of Agriculture. The marketing of irradiated fish fillets, for instance, would bring about a radical departure from existing fresh fish distribution practices. At present most of the fresh fish landed in Boston, for example, is sold within a 200-mile radius of that city. Although some fresh fish is sold in all American cities, most inland markets sell frozen fish because it offers more variety, better quality, and often lower price. But the subtle effect of taste is still a factor, and it is apparently not affected by radiation pasteurization.

The demand-supply picture would be changed dramatically if irradiators might be placed on a "mother ship" to provide a light dose of 100,000 rads to whole fish soon after the catch was landed and reduce bacterial populations; another pasteurization dose could be applied later, after processing and packaging has been completed at shore plants. Fishermen could thus operate at greater distances from home ports and stay out for longer periods.

The cost of irradiated fish over nonirradiated fish would be raised only by the cost of the radiation process. This, however, is not expected to be greater than the present cost of freezing. A survey of processors indicate that a cost of ¼ to 1¢ per pound for irradiation would be acceptable; more than half said they would be able to assume a 1 to 3¢ per pound cost increase. It is believed such higher expenditures would be balanced by increased markets and reduced losses.

Friend and Foe of Man

So much for "poisoning the sea" and "enriching the sea" with the same potential technique—the atom. Through indiscriminate use of oceanic fallout or dumping of wastes, nuclear energy can be highly dangerous; but under control, the atom can become a friend of man, with myriad benefits.

But the atom is not the only factor to watch at sea. As Seabrook Hull, in his *The Bountiful Sea* (Prentice-Hall, 1964) points out:

> "The balance between life and no life is precarious indeed, for if life is dependent on chemicals in trace quantities, so might it be destroyed by the introduction and dispersion throughout the ocean of trace quantities of such things as the all-too-indestructible household detergents, insecticides, industrial waste, human sewage, fuel oil from ships, and all the other wastes of civilized man.
>
> "Pesticides, defoliants, and other widely used materials

may maintain their chemical integrity through a large number of biological cycles, each of which raises the concentration. For example, DDT has been found in the oil of fish far at sea, in concentrations of over 300 parts per million—which is at lesat 45 times the legal tolerance permitted in foods for human consumption. Oysters are great assimilators of DDT—significant because most oyster beds occur in estuaries where DDT is likely to be high because of river runoff. . . . The byword of man's operations in the sea should be: 'When in doubt, don't.' Too little is known to predict the impact of some of the thing we now do, or contemplate doing."

Sea Studies Launched

Scientific study of pollution from rivers, lakes, estuaries, and other fresh water sources has been increasing steadily for more than six decades, but only recently has this work been extended to include pollution in the open sea. Wastes from highly industrialized coastal areas have curtailed water uses and fishery resources. Concern is felt near big cities, especially those which lack rivers where pollution can be diluted and flushed into the sea, or where waste is disposed into the confined waters of partially landlocked bays. Examples are Los Angeles and San Diego, in arid southern California; Miami, Florida, located on Biscayne Bay, and to an increasing extent, along Chesapeake and Delaware Bays.

Large volumes of industrial and treated domestic sewage, poured directly into the sea off Los Angeles, became such a problem in 1943 that several miles of bathing beaches were closed periodically until 1951, because of high bacterial counts in the surf zones. Then a new disposal plant was opened at Hyperion and restrictions were lifted from the beach. But the staggering population increases in the Los Angeles area may require a renewal of limitations or some additional measures.

Recently a sludge outfall was opened, extending seven miles into the Pacific, off Los Angeles, to a depth of 300 feet. A second outfall, five miles in length, has been approved for liquid effluent. Part of the basic research necessary for the engineering installations was done at the Allan Hancock Foundation, using the research vessel *Valero IV*, University of Southern California.

Potential pollution problems in southern California are of

such magnitude that the State of California Water Pollution Control Board initiated a five-year research study in 1956. This survey was undertaken by a research team of twelve scientists, studying 250 miles of coastal shelf from the intertidal zone down to depths of 300 feet. This basic program was designed to discover the properties and seasonal fluctuations of inshore water masses, the kinds, numbers and distribution of animals and plants in the water and on the sea bottom, and the kinds of distribution of sediments on the bottom.

All of these fundamentals were necessary, according to J. Laurens Barnard, of the Allan Hancock Foundation, writing in *Sea Frontiers*.

> "In designing new sewage installations, engineers require detailed information on the direction and speed of ocean currents in order to assess the rate at which the waste will be diluted and dispersed.
>
> "They must know the fluctuations in the depth of the thermocline, which is the water depth where temperature changes quickly from warm to cool. Just as atmospheric pollutants are held down by a thermocline in air, so ocean wastes can be held at depth by the thermocline and thus are dispersed without floating to the surface.
>
> "Engineers need to know also the sea water temperature at the bottom, so that they can predict the cooling effect th water has on the outfall pipe and its waste. The waste must be cooled to a temperature below that of the thermocline, to keep it from surfacing. Thus, the longer the pipe, the more time for cooling of the waste."

While these physical problems have been studied with some success, virtually nothing is known about bottom animals and how they are organized into communities, or about their usefulness as food or for sports fisheries. Research into this phase revealed the amazing fact that more than half of the 2,000 kinds of bottom animals found in the region examined by the Allan Hancock Foundation were completely unknown to science.

The sea is becoming the repository of more trash from rivers, even from those streams which flow freely. Floating beer cans once used to disintegrate but now they are rustproof; paper cups and plates formerly became soggy and disappeared, but now they are plastic-coated. In the summer, algae flourishes on nitrates and phosphates in the effluent covering water near the shore and bordering it with a thick green smelly scum, which later sinks or moves slowly out to sea.

$1 Billion Bond Issue in New York

So serious has become the problem of water pollution in New York State that Governor Nelson A. Rockefeller has called for a $1 billion state bond issue to help finance a vast six-year program aimed at ending pollution of lakes, streams, and rivers, much of which ends in the sea as a menace to health, beaches, and shipping. This new pure-water program will end Rockefeller's cherished pay-as-you-go policy. The state and federal governments would each pick up 30 per cent of the cost while the localities would pay only 40 per cent. In order to get the job under way as quickly as possible, Rockefeller agreed that the state would prefinance the federal share.

The Governor estimates the cost of building local sewage-treatment plants and interceptor sewers between now and 1979 would be $1.7 billion. He suggested the federal government get into the program by eliminating what he calls "discriminations" in present federal grant-in-aid programs for new sewerage-treatment plants and interceptor sewers. Federal law limits to $600,000 the amount of aid which may be granted to a locality for a single project.

A Major Enigma

Although a great deal has been learned about waste disposal in seawater, the effort thus far has more clearly defined the problems than solved them. The Atomic Energy Commission, the Public Health Service, and other agencies have initiated studies designed to clarify the role of atomic and other wastes in the environment and as they may affect man's health.

Poisoning the sea is still a major problem, and it shows no sign of diminishing. "Biological problems are the most complex," according to Dr. I. E. Wallen, assistant director for oceanography at the Smithsonian Institution. In essence, says Wallen in *Ocean Sciences* (U.S. Naval Institute),

> "An evaluation of a waste effluent must identify the populations; learn the life cycles, feeding mechanisms

and nutrient requirements of each species; study the tolerance of each species for the various harmful portions of the wastes; know the physical-chemical parameters and interrelationships of sea water, sediments and wastes as related to their dilution; and understand the optimum balance between desirable addition of wastes and nutrients and any possible detriment to man's activities."

This, admittedly, is a big job and a most involved one. Dr. Wallen agrees that:

"Although the number of fascinating research problems is legion, the nature of the problems is so complex that many years will be required to attain a reasonably full understanding of the effects of human and industrial wastes on the ocean, and the routes of their return to man."

CHAPTER VIII

BIRTHPLACE OF STORMS

ALL BIG STORMS are born at sea. That is, all the really large ones—the hurricanes, the typhoons, the "baguios" (Philippines), the "reppus" (Japan), the "willy-willies" (western Australia), the "asifa-a" (Arabian coasts), and other large atmospheric disturbances—begin in warm tropical waters not too far north and south of the Equator. After erratic courses, they usually die when they reach continental land masses, or colder seas. In some instances, however, they may continue inland for many miles, and, in rare instances, they may bend back over the water again to vanish finally at sea, as did Hurricane "Dora," September 1964.

Observe the tracks of hurricanes over several years as they weave along from origin to death and you will note that no two courses are *exactly* alike, although there is a rough similar pattern of most tracks following North Atlantic hurricanes. First they swing west, then north, and then easterly, as a rule. Long lulls, brief halts, loops and double loops, and rebuilding of weakened storms are exceptions to the rules, making hurricane-forecasting one of the trickiest of all trades.

Despite the achievements in meteorology, and a growing network of communications warnings and safety precautions, every new hurricane is a potential killer and a destroyer of millions of dollars worth of property and natural resources. As more and more of the coastlines are being filled up and crowded with people, these major storms attract more attention, not only for better warnings, but also for efforts to modify, dissipate, and possibly eliminate such diastrous events.

Large Revolving Storms

This truly is a perplexing situation—one that has been demanded from man as long as the sea winds have blown on this planet. To simplify it a bit, let us concentrate on hurricane lore, because hurricane activities are similar to other major disturbances, and studies about them have been more extensive than those about any other kinds of storms.

To the expert, hurricanes are "large revolving storms, accompanied by violent destructive winds, heavy rains, and high waves and tides. They originate in tropical Atlantic areas, except in the South Atlantic, and usually move from low to higher altitudes with increasing speed, size and intensity."

Winds whirl counterclockwise in such storms, with the highest speeds in a circular band beginning at the edge of the "eye" and extending out 20 to 30 miles or more. In this area velocities may reach 150 miles an hour, with brief gusts at even higher speeds. At the mysterious center there is usually a small, cloudless core from 5 to 20 miles across. This core is called the "eye" since the sky there is often clear, or only partly clouded, and the winds are usually very light. Before the full character of hurricanes was known, many lives were lost when people left their shelters, or when ships reset sails during this deceptive period. The destructive winds of a hurricane may extend across a path from 25 to 500 miles wide. As the storm develops and moves forward, it may travel a path several thousand miles long.

Greatest Loss of Life—Drowning

While hurricanes do not have the force of quick localized tornadoes, they cause immense damage, toppling trees, blowing over houses and small buildings, tearing down power and telephone wires and antennas, and even blowing trains off their tracks. The greatest loss of life during hurricanes, however, is caused by drowning. As the storm moves relentlessly forward, it often piles up huge waves which cut off or completely cover low-lying beaches and small islands. In fact, the ocean level may rise 6 feet or more in a few minutes, preventing escape. Small boats are flung high on beaches. Giant combers pound and smash shore buildings, docks, roads, and bridges, and may wash away long-standing sand dunes and broad causeways.

Worst of all, most hurricanes are accompanied by torrential rains, which trap motorists and livestock and cause huge damage by flooding and destroying crops and wrecking low-lying communities. Tons of water overflow rivers, canals, ditches, and gutters, and will stand for hours after the deluge has passed.

By timely warnings, some of them by weather satellites, many lives and much property have been saved in recent years. The Weather Bureau is responsible for issuing warnings of hurricanes which approach the United States mainland. During the summer and fall months when most hurricanes occur, forecast offices at San Juan, Miami, New Orleans, Washington, and Boston install special emergency communications facilities and maintain a careful watch for the development of all tropical storms and hurricanes.

Give It a Name

As soon as there are definite indications from a ship or a plane that a hurricane is forming, even though it is reported a thousand miles or more from the mainland, the nascent storm is given a name, such as "Donna" or "Hazel" or "Cleo," (to avoid confusion if two or more tropical storms occur at the same time) and the Weather Bureau begins issuing "advisories." The advisories, issued frequently throughout the day and night, tell just where the storm is, how intense it is, and its speed and probable direction of movement. These advisory messages are radioed to ships at sea, so that they can steer clear of the storm, and to small isolated islands in the storm's path, so that their residents can be evacuated or take other precautions.

If the hurricane moves toward the mainland, hurricane watch notices, around the clock, are included in the advisories, and storm and hurricane warnings are issued. In addition, bulletins for press, radio, and television are issued at frequent intervals to keep the public informed.

When a hurricane threatens any portion of the United States coast, special emergency warning centers are set up at Weather Bureau offices in the threatened areas. Representatives of newspapers, radio and television stations, Civil Defense, Red Cross, city governments, etc. come to the center to obtain firsthand information on the storm. Radio amateurs and special telephone and radio lines are used so that this vital information can be quickly disseminated. Special observations are taken of land stations at frequent intervals. Radiosonde instruments carried by balloons, normally used every 12 hours, are sent aloft more frequently to measure conditions up to 60,000 feet above the earth; reports from ships at sea are requested as often as once an hour.

Hurricane Hunters

Helpful as these special observations are, the most vital source of data are the reports from the specially equipped Air Force and Navy reconnaissance airplanes and Weather Bureau research aircraft. Since the Hurricane Warning Service was reorganized in 1935, these courageous "Hurricane Hunters" have patrolled areas hundreds of miles from land, often penetrating to the center of storms, to obtain precise information on the location and movements of hurricanes. Also taking part, in the line of regular duty, are the planes and cutters of the Coast Guard, which often must penetrate the fringes of such storms during necessary search and rescue missions.

Another means of detecting major storms is by radar equipment, installed at various coastal points. During the past few years radar sets have picked up typical rain bands of a hurricane as far as 200 miles beyond the land, and have followed the tracks continuously. As the number of radar stations increases, the accuracy of this method of spotting hurricanes will improve.

140 • NEW WORLDS OF OCEANOGRAPHY

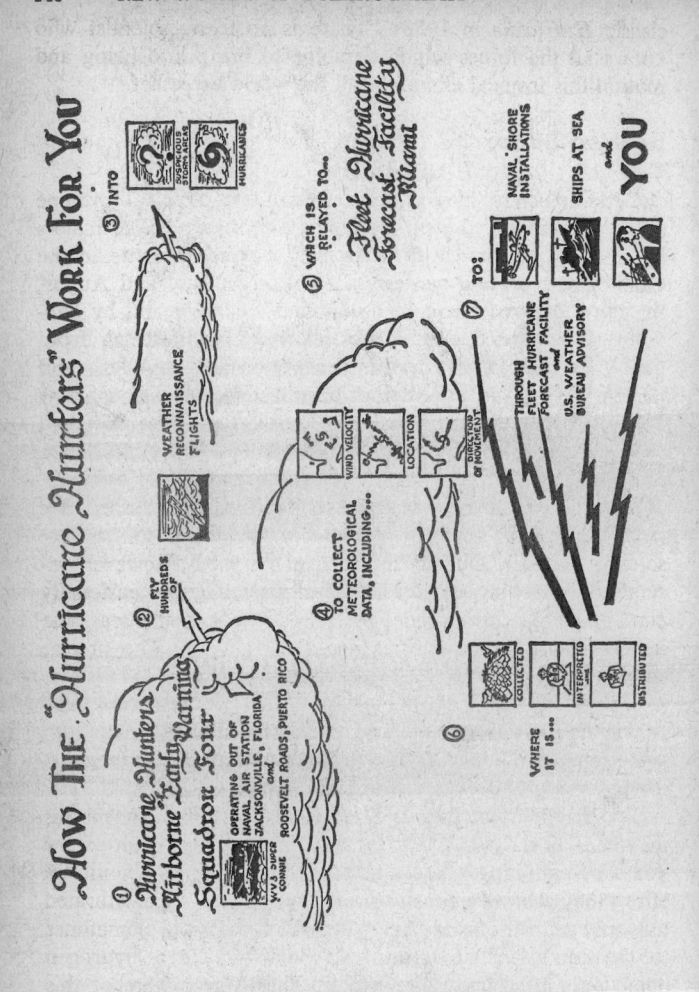

Ever since hurricanes ravaged the Spanish Main and sent thousands of treasure galleons and other unwarned vessels to their doom, man has been trying to locate the *exact origins* of hurricanes at sea. Scientists have various theories about their precise birthplaces, but because no one has yet sat down on the spot where one actually began, we must rely upon bits of circumstantial evidence which come from various sources. As Marjory Stoneman Douglas said in her classic *Hurricane* in 1958: "There is no living scientist who knows all the forces which combine to bring into being and motion this tropical climax of all the world's weather."

Hopping During the "Season"

Geographically, the principal regions of tropical cyclone origin vary widely during the hurricane "season." The majority of early season (May and June) storms originate in the Gulf of Mexico and western Caribbean. In July and August the areas of most frequent origin shift eastward and by September are located over the broad seas which stretch from the Bahamas southeastward to the Lesser Antilles, and thence far eastward to south of the Cape Verde Islands, near the west coast of Africa. After mid-September, the principal regions of origin swing back again to the western Caribbean and the Gulf of Mexico.

During most of the year, the two great oceans of earth—the sea and the atmosphere—conduct their intercourse in a most salutory manner. During the hurricane seasons, however, instead of offsetting each other's energies, they occasionally combine forces in a tirade, as it were, against the seas, the land, and all their creatures and their devices. The precise mechanics that kick up these uproars is still a mystery. Among the factors—the Bermuda "high," the westerlies, and the easterlies—changes in pattern occur; then gradually they build up and bingo! The next thing we know a hurricane is on its way.

Technically what happens, we believe, is this: air masses move across the vast ocean expanses under the action of the hot sun, collecting great amounts of water vapor until, in effect, they achieve a supersaturated condition—supersaturated not only with moisture, but with energy as well, sometimes to the equivalent of forces that would make a hydrogen bomb resemble a mere firecracker. The biggest share of this energy is in the form of the latent heat of vaporization of the moisture content of the atmosphere.

What Triggers It?

What finally triggers a hurricane—starting this violent release of energy—isn't known, but efforts are being made to do something about it, once it has started. This project is known as Stormfury, a joint Department of Commerce Weather Bureau-Department of the Navy program of scientific experiments designed to discover and test methods of *modifying* hurricanes. Project Stormfury developed directly from studies conducted by the Weather Bureau's National Hurricane Research, established in 1956 as a result of the hurricane catastrophes of 1954 and 1955. It began only as a means of increasing scientific knowledge of hurricanes and improving methods of hurricane prediction. Since 1956, much new information on hurricanes has been found; the findings point to promising experiments in modification, that is, possibly in dissolving, diverting, or retarding a hurricane.

From observations gathered in hurricanes by aircraft, radar, and balloon-borne instruments, meteorologists have found that large quantities of liquid water or droplets are present above the freezing level—virtually to the tops of the clouds forming the eye wall. Visual and radar observations indicated that a relatively small "chimney" near the eye serves as the primary cell of the hurricane. This chimney is the main connection between the lower inflow and the outflow layer of the storm. These discoveries suggest that the balance of forces in the hurricane might be altered by seeding in this small area (perhaps no larger than 200 square miles) and causing the conversion of liquid water into ice crystals. In the process, energy is released in the form of latent heat of fusion.

First Large-scale Seeding

In 1961, the Weather Bureau and the National Science Foundation agreed to sponsor a series of hurricane-seeding experiments. About the same time, the U.S. Naval Ordnance Test Station at China Lake, California, developed a new silver iodide generator, suitable for use in seeding hurricanes. The Navy offered to supply the generators as well as aircraft to drop them into the storm. This bomb-like device creates a dense sheet of silver iodide smoke extending to the ocean, and in seconds fills a cloud with a vast number of large silver iodide particles.

Hurricanes themselves, however, are not too plentiful. Some years they do not come near the mainland, which suit most people very well, but not scientists, who need a great deal more information about hurricanes before they can determine whether experts are getting results from their experiments or from some still unknown natural behavior of hurricanes.

Seeding operations were conducted during Hurricane "Esther" on two consecutive days in September 1961. Principal objectives: to test the silver iodide seeding technique and to determine: (1) whether a large amount of supercooled liquid water would be converted to ice under the turbulent conditions present in hurricanes, (2) whether artificial strategic release of latent heat of fusion could create instabilities in the storm; and (3) whether a reduction in maximum wind speeds would result.

"Hot Towers"

According to present analysis, the primary energy cell of a hurricane is the eye, where updrafts called "hot towers," may rise to altitudes in excess of 50,000 feet. Efforts now are first being aimed at destroying this *structure* to learn more of the mechanics of an in-being hurricane rather than attempting to control or to explode the entire storm.

To do this, the closed-in wall area was seeded by silver iodide generators, launched from aircraft flying at 20,000 feet and higher during the September 1961 tests—the first truly scientific attempt to knock out one of nature's biggest punches. As predicted, water rimming the hurricane's eye turned to ice, and maximum wind speeds dropped about 10 per cent. But it was only a glancing blow, for the effects lasted only a short while, and similar changes often occur naturally.

Project Stormfury was continued for another year, but the mild hurricane season of 1962 provided no real opportunity for repeating the iodide-seeding experiments. However, a "dry run" was conducted on Hurricane "Daisy" when it was off the Florida Coast.

Experiments in 1963 Vary

During the season of 1963, on August 23 and 24, scientists of Project Stormfury tried again. Following the seeding on the 23rd, winds continued to increase. But on the days after the seeding of the 24th the storm did decrease somewhat. Project scientists again cautioned that these changes have occurred in other hurricanes when there have been no seeding experiments. They cited "Arlene," the first hurricane of 1963, as an example of an unseeded hurricane in which very abrupt changes occurred naturally. They stressed that experiments, such as those conducted in Hurricanes "Beulah" (1963) and "Esther" (1961), must be repeated several times, and that the measurements must constantly be compared with unmodified hurricanes, before any real scientific conclusions can be reached.

In 1963 only Hurricane "Beulah" was seeded. Other hurricanes, because of their uncertain state of development or their inappropriate locations were not seeded. Nor was any seeding done in 1964, although the natural behavior of all hurricanes was studied by instrument from aircraft and at other facilities within access.

Recent studies indicate that a horizontal phase of cloud seeding may be more exciting and possibly more rewarding than the first, or vertical, phase. For practical weather modification, this second phase could prove the more significant, since great clouds are the combustion cylinders in hurricanes, the equatorial "firebox" of the global air circulation, and important in the radiation budget of an entire region. But many experiments beyond this and other studies must be made many times before science can be sure a series of controls can be established. Malkus and Simpson in their recent (1964) *Modification Experiments on Tropical Cumulus Clouds* conclude: "It has long been deplored that the earth sciences must be observational rather than experimental sciences. Here meteorology is taking the first small steps toward becoming an experimental science, which it must become if man is ever to exert real control on his atmosphere."

Stormfury Carries On

Meanwhile, Project Stormfury will continue to be supported by Navy personnel of the Hurricane Hunter Squadron based on Roosevelt Roads, Puerto Rico, and the Heavy Attack Squadron based at Sanford, Florida, as well as by the Naval Ordnance Test Station, China Lake, California, which designed and developed the silver iodide canisters. The National Weather Modification Program, which includes research and testing of major storms, totalled $4.6 million in fiscal 1962. This sum was spread among nine federal agencies.

Scientists agree they need to know much more about how nature *makes* weather, before they can hope to *control* it to any great extent. How, for instance, does nature take a vast area of humidity and wrap it up into a cloud? Then, how do 7 or 8 million tiny water droplets inside the cloud suddenly form raindrops heavy enough to fall all the way to the ground? At its General Circulations Research Laboratory, in Washington, D.C., the Weather Bureau is in the midst of an even more ambitious project. It is trying to translate into a set of mathematical equations the recipe nature itself uses to cook up the weather. In fact, the new awareness of the awesome power of nature and the complexity of the earth's weather-factory has brought about what the National Science Foundation calls "a general back-to-the-laboratory movement" in meteorology!

New High-in-the-Sky Factor

While we have been predicting weather conditions and have also been trying to modify storms, a brand new factor has come into the equation: weather satellites. Weather forecasters point out that satellites do not *forecast* conditions, but rather *observe* them. Nevertheless their high altitude pictures give part of the information needed to compile an accurate forecast.

Five years ago (1960) such projects were in the experimental stages; today they play an integral part in weather forecasting. The first satellite in the Tiros series, launched by rocket in April 1, 1960, marked the beginning of one of America's most successful satellite ventures. All eight satellites have performed far beyond their normal expectation of three or four months, providing a wide range of weather data—details about air fronts, thunderstorms, cloud patterns, and moist air regions. In each case, pictures from two highly sensitive cameras were fed to recording machines. Facts were then transmitted to earth, much like a pretaped television show, when the satellite came into range of a monitoring tower.

A satellite "weather space station" itself resembles an oversized hat box. Its 18 sides are covered with more than 9,000 tiny mirrorlike solar cells that recharge its powerful operating batteries from the sun. *Nimbus I,* an advanced weather observation station, takes pictures of a 1,500-by-500 mile area, using three cameras. Synchronized with the sun, *Nimbus I* provides day-by-day observation of a broad specific region, a feat that the early Tiros satellites could not achieve.

How Satellites Save Money

Previously, when a hurricane storm cell was spotted, planes flew into the eye, or center, of the developing storm to check wind intensity and pressure. Planes were dispatched routinely every six hours during the hurricane season. The new observation system by satellites saves time and money, because the pilot can quickly pinpoint the area of a storm before taking off.

By tracking storms as they develop, meteorologists can prepare forecasts as much as two days earlier than by older methods. One of the most dramatic examples of the value of getting advance weather information by satellite was the evacuation of 350,000 people from the path of Hurricane "Carla" in Texas and Louisiana, in September 1961. Early warning made it possible to prepare the largest mass evacuation in the United States and to save many lives. From July 1961 to June 1964, in the Atlantic alone, satellites detected 10 storms and tracked 18 others.

The excellent performance of the *Nimbus I*, which shot into orbit August 28, 1964, has enthusiastic scientists at the Goddard Space Flight Center predicting that the day may soon come when satellites and computers will replace the weatherman—or almost! This 830-pound storm-hunting satellite is equipped with television cameras similar to those that transmitted *Ranger 7*'s closeup pictures of the moon. Pictures of cloud formations at midnight over the Philippines and of Siberian rivers were only a few of the unique achievements of *Nimbus I*, which is giving the National Aeronautics and Space Administration worldwide photo coverage of the earth's surface and atmospheric conditions. The night pictures were taken with infrared sensors.

Nimbus II, successor to *Nimbus I*, will probably go up in 1965, with even more advanced sensors designed to measure temperatures and atmospheric components. The ultimate goal of the Nimbus project is to have satellites transmitting such complete and precise data that the information can be fed directly into a computer, which will then come up with a weather prediction.

Overcomes Earth Drag

Meanwhile, a new weather satellite, *Tiros IX*, was launched from Cape Kennedy early in 1965. It includes a number of significant advances in the already successful Tiros series, which eventually will become part of a Tiros Operation System (TOS), planned for 1966. These satellites will do almost *anything*, it seems—their surveys including weather forecasting, sea ice reconnaissance, storm warning, and even locust control.

Best of all, *Tiros IX* adjusts in orbit to keep the cameras pointed toward the earth, affording complete photographic coverage of the world's weather. Unlike the other Tiros satellites, the orbits of which carried them around the world in a roughly east-west direction, *Tiros IX* moves in a primarily north-south plane. As a result, the orbit does not change its position in respect to the sun. Each camera snaps its shutter only when it is pointed directly at the earth. With its two cameras, the satellite is able to take a picture of the earth once every three seconds, if necessary.

Another unusual aspect about *Tiros IX* is that it can maintain a constant spin rate, overcoming the drag caused by the earth's magnetism. To counteract this drag, a 30-inch-long magnetic coil acts directly against the earth's magnetism. Thus the spin rate can be kept almost constant by sending small charges of electric current through the coil. As a backup, a small rocket system has been installed in the satellite, in case the original system does not work.

"Project Cold Low"

Study of thousands of satellite photographs has led meteorologists at the Weather Bureau's National Weather Satellite Center to suspect that certain cloud patterns indicate cyclonic circulations, or eddies, at high altitudes in the atmosphere, which may later develop downward to the surface and become hurricanes. A new hurricane investigation, called "Project Cold Low," will be initiated soon to carry it out. It is so called because temperatures in these high-level eddies are usually lower than in the surrounding atmosphere. When cold lows are detected in satellite pictures, research aircraft will be dispatched to gather data in the area. If the scientists' suspicion proves to be correct, Project Cold Low will provide unique new data on the earliest stages of hurricane formation.

Data from weather satellites are already being considered for other unusual uses. Rangers may soon depend on satellites to help them spot forest fires. African farmers hope satellites can locate and determine the paths of locust swarms. Mariners plan to use them for ice reconnaissance.

When the time arrives that we can change at will the direction of major storms, Navy scientists have some plans to use them as weapons against hostile fleets. An ability to control the weather could bring greater changes in warfare than did the explosion of the first nuclear bomb, says Vice Admiral William F. Raborn, formerly the Navy's development chief.

Weather in Warfare

"We already have taken our first steps toward developing an environmental warfare capability," said Admiral Raborn, the man credited with pushing the Polaris missile-firing submarine to combat readiness in record time. "We are using satellite weather data from *Tiros II* for current tactical operations and more accurate long-range weather predictions," Admiral Raborn said in the *U.S. Naval Institute Proceedings*, a semi-official journal which often serves to air the views of professional Navy officers. He added: "Some experiments in fog dissipation have shown promise, and some exploratory research has been conducted on ways to change the heading of major storms. The capability to change the direction of destructive storms and to guide them may well inflict greater damage than could an enemy's gunfire and missiles."

Because scientific advances make it possible, Admiral Raborn said, the Navy is now planning a 10-year study of the atmosphere. The study bears the name ATMOS, and will be coordinated with separate secret research on the oceans and their depths. The Navy poses these possibilities: (1) ground, sea, air, and amphibious operations might be aided by driving away rain or clouds; (2) conversely, creation of solid, low overcasts might be used to hide troop concentrations and movements and the deployment of naval task forces: (3)

large-scale weather control techniques might be used to cause extensive flooding in strategic land areas, or even to bring a new "ice age" upon the enemy.

Most Complicated of Sciences

Any actual control of weather is admittedly some distance away, but weather predictions will soon be better than educated guesswork. This news comes from a report by the National Academy of Sciences, the senate of American science. Rightfully, the academy says, weather science appears to be the most complicated of all the sciences. Progress has been slow, partly because of inadequacy of observations. But the new weather satellites, plus other readings from the surface and upper air, relayed to collating stations for comparison with local data and earlier observations, may meet many of today's deficiencies. Already millions of bits of data are taken daily at 20,000 synoptic—simultaneously observing and reporting—stations around the world. But the network does not reach many areas of the earth, which is why weather prediction is still so unpredictable.

The Academy report urges a vast research effort, on a national scale, to be carried cooperatively by government agencies, universities, and private foundations, at a total estimated cost of about $2 billion. This is a lot of money, but it is a small investment indeed considering the great potentialities of any real weather *control*. It is a mere pittance, in fact, when we match it with the billions upon billions of dollars that hurricane catastrophes have cost this country in property losses, suffering, and inconvenience, plus uncountable thousands of lives.

Meanwhile, the Department of Commerce and the National Aeronautics and Space Administration have signed an agreement defining the roles their agencies will follow in the development of the National Operational Meteorological Satellite System. Expected to be in operation in 1965, this system will provide global weather information daily for use by meteorological services throughout the world in improving weather forecasts. Such a joint program should save an estimated $125 million over a five-year period, compared with earlier plans. The system is being designed to meet the United States' present military needs for the Department of Defense and for civilian weather satellite observations.

At the moment, however, the greatest need in advancing the weather services is not *instrumentation* but *people*—a much greater number of scientists trained in the field of meteorology. A huge amount of skilled, very laborious, work will soon be required. Training of men, and women, too, to do it will be very largely up to the universities, only a few of which now provide adequate courses in these fields.

Here again is another available opportunity in budding science—an oceanographic challenge both for new teachers, and for today's youth.

CHAPTER IX

MAKING FISHERIES PAY

FISHING HAS CHANGED very little since the first fish was caught by man. It is still a hunting process. Although fishing has been aided by individual experience and methods, most fishermen still rely primarily on blind searching for fish, and, with few exceptions, on fumbling inefficient ways of catching them. Electronic equipment now is used successfully in some fisheries to locate the resource, but most fishermen depend upon experience, and often upon actual sightings, to locate their quarry. The catching process either is completely passive, depending on fish to blunder into the gear, or active in the sense that it attracts the fish with bait, or overtakes or surrounds them with nets.

Obviously these are essentially the fishing methods of antiquity. The only substantial change has been the advent of motive power. But this has merely increased the range of operation, by permitting use of larger gear or by improving navigation and requiring less time enroute to and from fishing grounds. The fishing industry is still very much at the mercy of the weather, which interferes directly with fish location and catching, damages gear, alters normal patterns of distribution and migration, and causes large seasonal and annual variations in actual abundance of the resource.

MAKING FISHERIES PAY • 151

GILL NET
North Atlantic

GILL NETTER HAULING THE NET

ALUMINUM FLOATS

LEAD LINE

BUOYS

FISHING AT 20–40 FATHOMS FOR COD, HADDOCK, AND POLLOCK.

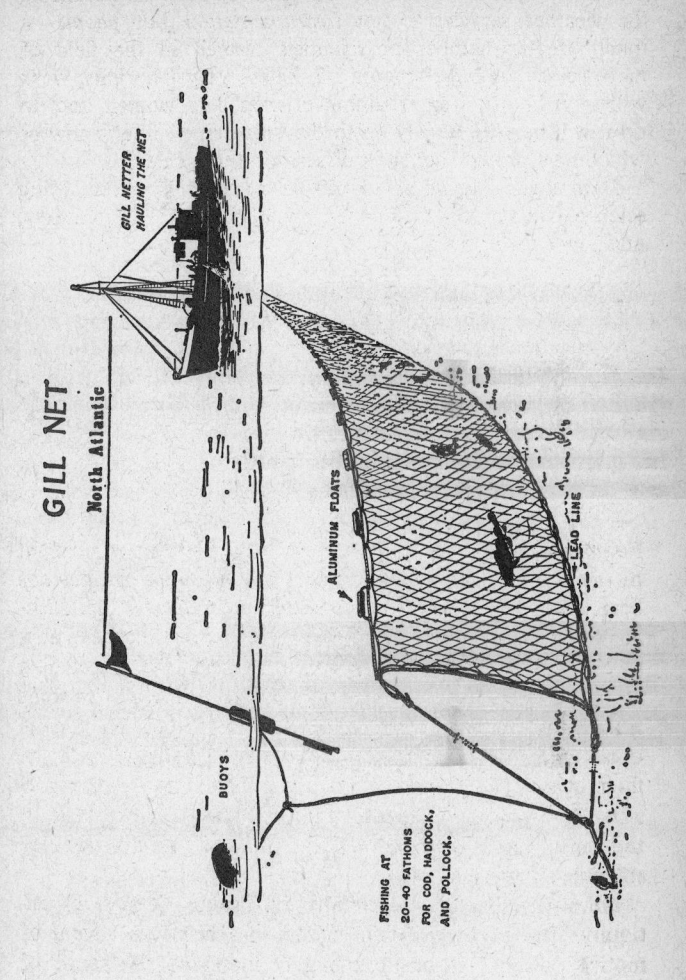

New Factor: the Fishery Scientist

As in any other business, time is valuable. Much of a fisherman's time is wasted in *searching* for his catch. Modern fishing requires expensive boats, and salaries for men to operate them. So every minute saved is valuable to both the fisherman and the consumer. Two kinds of information are necessary: (1) the fisherman needs a method to locate fish quickly once he is in their vicinity; and (2) he needs more general knowledge on the whereabouts of fish of desirable size and how this distribution changes in time and space. The engineer can help him with the first objective; the second is a problem for a comparatively new factor, the fishery scientist.

The primitive state of today's fishing operations is evident when we contrast it with today's prosperous and highly scientific *agriculture*, particularly in the United States. America would not have become the world's leading nation if we had been content to subsist on the natural plant and animal production of the land. Perhaps our culture would not have risen much above that of native Indian tribes if this had been the case.

Why Not Farm the Sea?

Yet our only successful attempts at farming the sea have been developed in the oyster and clam fisheries. Even the most advanced shellfish culture operations in the United States are primitive compared with our least well-developed land farming methods. The history of our shellfish industry demonstrates clearly the need for overall or widespread improvement, for, according to Dr. J. L. McHugh, assistant director for Biological Research, Bureau of Commercial Fisheries, our total fishery production is declining steadily.

Perhaps our rudimentary fishing techniques can be illustrated by a few examples. Our tuna industry, one of the few relatively efficient segments of our commercial fisheries, still relies principally on visual sighting to locate tuna schools. Our purse seine fishery off the west coasts of North and South America, which takes most of the American tuna catch, finds its fish by watching for bird flocks or the activity of porpoises. Sea birds are a limited magnet, because their numbers diminish quickly with increasing distance from shore. Hence, even this indirect method of location is not effective in many parts of the high seas where tuna are known to abound.

Again according to McHugh, American fishermen cannot compete economically with Japanese fishermen in the tuna long-line fishery, the best method yet developed for fishing tuna in many parts of the world. Long-line fisheries need lots of labor, which is cheap and plentiful in Oriental seas, but not elsewhere. To remain competitive, and to increase the catch in proportion to increasing demand for tuna, American tuna fleets must be assisted to develop new methods to locate and catch fish. What are the best methods is a major problem confronting oceanographers, technicians, marine biologists, and engineers, working separately and together.

Which Fishes Weigh Most?

The United States menhaden fishery, which lands a greater weight of fish than any other North American fishery, takes most of its catch with purse seines. The fish are located visually, either from the crow's nest of the fishing vessel, or from small airplanes. The school is surrounded by a net, which is then closed at the bottom, and the fish are dipped or pumped into the hold of the vessel.

Menhaden fishing has been improved by using electricity to remove fish from the net. In preparation, an anode is attached to the end of a large hose through which the live fish are to be pumped from the net into the boat, and a cathode is dropped to the bottom of the net. When the current is turned on, the fish swim toward the anode, relieving the strain on the net and speeding the hauling and pumping process. It has not yet been found feasible to substitute electricity for the laborious and costly netting operation, although theoretically this is not impossible. Modern technology has somewhat improved the efficiency of locating and catching menhaden, but more oceanographic research and technological methods must improve these operations even more to make better use of this nonedible fish, so much desired for use as fertilizer.

The most important fishing gear in terms of the landed value of a catch, and the second more important in terms of landed weight, are the otter trawls. Basically this gear is a simple bag of netting, forced open as it is dragged along the bottom by water pressure against two "otter boards," one at

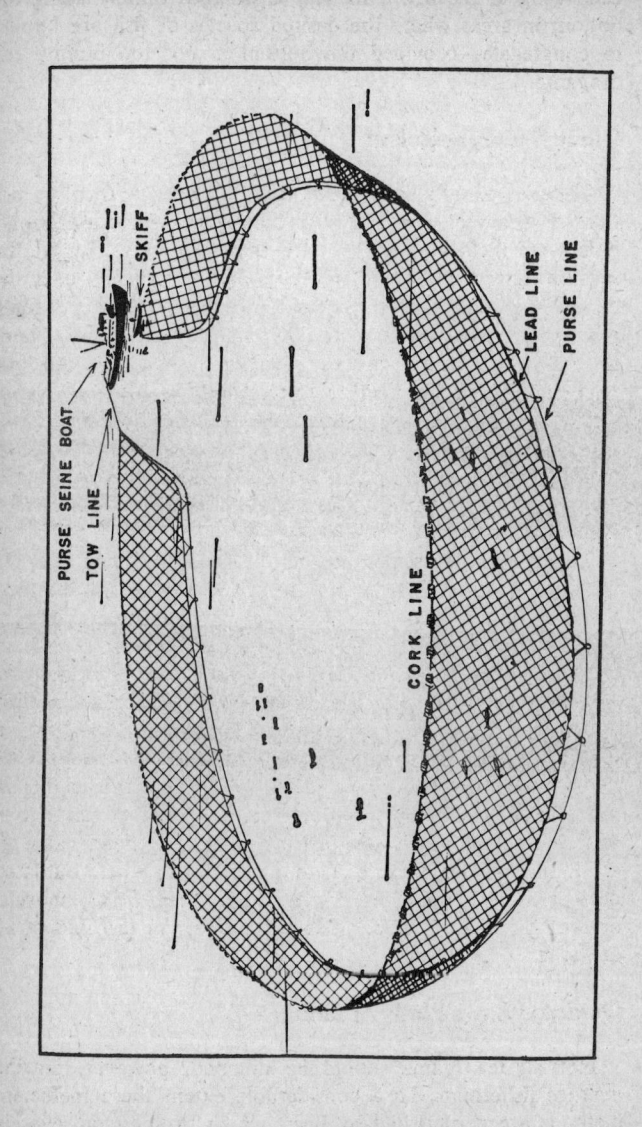

Purse Seine Net

each wing of the net. This gear is dragged blindly along the bottom in areas where the desired species of fish are known to congregate—provided the bottom is not too bumpy for dragging.

Otters Quite Inefficient

Fisheries experts, who have observed such a trawl in action by means of diving gear or underwater television, report it is quite inefficient. Fish that come within the path of the net are herded in front of it; some dodge vertically over the head rope, some dodge laterally around the wings, some escape by burrowing into the bottom. Only some of the herd fall back into the net and cannot escape. What can be done to increase the otter trawl's catch? Fishermen suggest enlarging the mouth of the net, or to speed the rate of hauling, but both present expensive difficulties. Many productive bottoms are too rough (rocks, reefs, wreckage) for successful trawling by larger or speedier gear. So here is another problem for modern fishery research.

Together, purse seines and otter trawls produced over 75 per cent of the total weight and nearly 50 per cent of the total value of fishery products landed at United States ports in 1963. The remainder of the catch was made by a variety of gears of a few basic types. In general (McHugh), there is an inverse relationship between efficiency of catching method and landed value per unit weight. Thus, some of our most valuable fishery resources, the fish most desired for table use, are harvested by almost incredibly antiquated and inefficient methods. Commerical fishery resources valued at more than $65 million, or nearly one-fifth of the total landed value of all United States fisheries, are caught with such outdated devices as hook and line, tongs, rakes, hoes, forks, shovels, or even by hand! Contrast these with other modern industrial methods.

Outdated Laws Partly to Blame

Not all the blame should be dumped, however, on the average fisherman. To a considerable extent these inefficient methods are perpetuated by laws, which prohibit or severely restrict the use of more effective techniques. Some of them are forced upon the industry by state laws. It is characteristic

156 • NEW WORLDS OF OCEANOGRAPHY

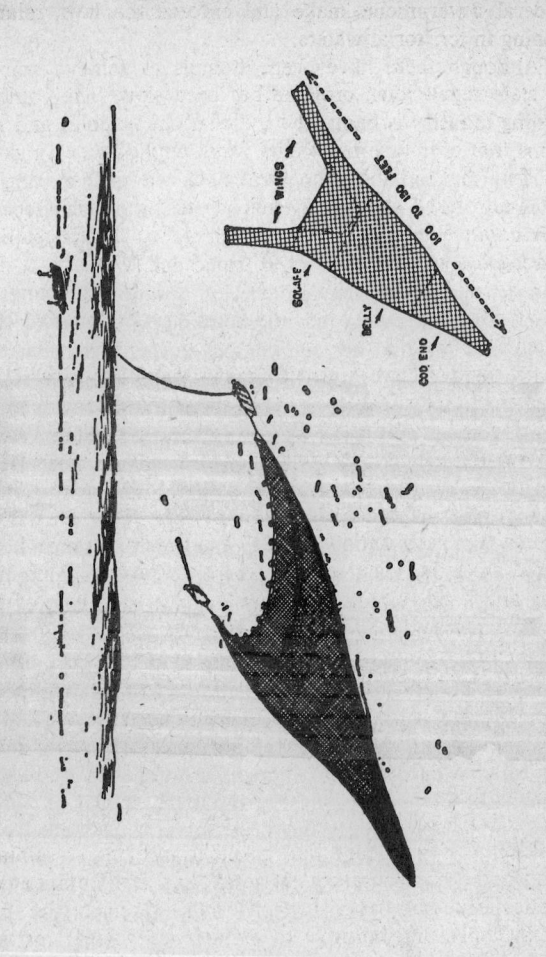

ATLANTIC OTTER TRAWL

of our form of government that the individual state, not the federal government, make and enforce the laws relating to fishing in territorial waters.

Although there have been attempts to achieve uniformity in state regulations, progress has been slow. The commercial fishing industry is hampered by local philosophies and regulations that often are in conflict when applied to a single stock of fish that inhabits the waters of more than one state. Common to all states is a tendency to favor inefficiency as a conservative measure, or as a method of dividing the catch among the greatest number of fishermen. Actually, such policies are in conflict with the United States system of private enterprise, for they raise the unit cost of production and often lead to a declining supply.

As already stated, purse seines and otter trawls, while inefficient, are still the best existing gear in the United States fishery, and, indeed, in the world. Yet the use of them is severely restricted in Maryland and Virginia. Otter trawling is not permitted in Chesapeake Bay by either state, and Maryland prohibits purse seining in all territorial waters off its shores. By such action the Chesapeake Bay states have favored more inefficient and costly methods, such as pound netting and hand seining, and have increased the cost of fishing certain species to the point that they cannot be harvested at a profit. Maryland's prohibition of purse seining has denied its citizens the benefits of sharing the menhaden harvest, and a fairly steady source of income that it would bring to the state.

Last Sail-Work Fleet

Oddly enough, Maryland's prohibition of purse seining has brought no compensatory economic benefits. Both states, but particularly Maryland, have virtually doomed the private shellfish planting industry to extinction by legal restrictions on free enterprise in the name of conservation. Nowhere else in the world does a law prohibit mechanical power on shellfish dredging vessels, although we shall have to admit that Maryland does perpetuate a colorful and beautiful sight with its sail-powered oyster-dredging fleet—the last such working fleet in the United States. For historic and aesthetic reasons, the preservation of this fleet might be justified on its own merits. But to perpetuate it as a necessary method of fishing, to maintain a fishery resource, is anachronistic in today's world.

Fish *quality* offers another big field for oceanographic research. It is well known that marine and fresh water animals undergo seasonal changes related to the sexual cycle and other factors. For example, the oil yield and quality of herring-like fishes varies widely with season and with age of the fish. Flavor, appearance, and volume of oyster meats vary to a considerable degree with season, age, and locality. We need to know a great deal more about such variables and their causes, and not just accept the tradition of refusing to use oysters in a month without "R's" (oysters in June, July, and August *are* edible; they are simply *leaner* during this rest period). The whole fisheries problem offers a challenge to the biologist and the food technologist to pool their knowledge and efforts.

As for farming the sea, we have barely begun. High labor costs along our coasts have caused us to lag far behind other nations in marine husbandry. Yet the need for animal protein will soon force the world to adopt ocean farming methods. The nation which leads the world in developing feasible new methods of food fisheries may well dominate world society in the not-too-distant future.

Few Life Histories

If oceanographic research is to produce the great advances we foresee in utilizing the living resources of the ocean, we need also to improve our scientific methods and techniques. It is important for the fishery scientist to be able to estimate at least the *relative* abundance, and if possible the *absolute* abundance, of fish at various stages of their lives. It is still extremely difficult to do these things, mainly because only a very few life-history stages of a small number of species has been compiled. Here is a challenge for the rising generation of oceanographers. It is difficult to imagine a development that would be of greater value to marine scientists and to the fishing industry than a satisfactory method of making an accurate census of sea animals.

The best indirect methods to conduct census studies to date has been to mark fish in various ways, and to estimate total abundance by the ratio of marked to unmarked fish in the catch. Fishes have been marked successfully by removing fins, tattooing, injection of harmless dyes, attachment of external tags or inserting of internal tags of plastic or metal. Recently scientists have experimented with a microscopic color-coded magnetic tag of extremely fine wire, and also by incorporating certain antibiotics in the diet of fish reared in hatcheries. Refined sonar techniques, or other electronic methods of direct counting, are future possibilities.

Changes Imposed by Nature

In addition to the changes on fisheries made by man (overfishing, pollution, radiation) there are the effects of changes imposed by nature. Variations in temperature, salinity, current patterns, and many unknown effects from underwater activity often upset the survival rates of marine life. Often these natural fluctations are confused with the effects of man's activities. Years of unusually good fishing, caused by successful spawning, often come in succession. When such a period is followed by years of below-average abundance, restrictive laws often are passed on the assumption that the decline is man-made.

Not necessarily so. Instead of filling the state legislatures with bills and legal restrictions, more attention might be employed profitably in oceanographic research and fishery investigations. The Bureau of Commercial Fisheries, with its own oceanic fleet at sea and its laboratories ashore in many parts of the nation, has already done much to remedy the neglect of *natural environment* as an important factor in fishery production.

Such research is difficult and costly, and results will not come quickly. It will be necessary to continue certain studies for many years, and to extend them into new and sometimes into unrewarded trials and errors, before changes in abundance and availability of fish, and their causes, are understood.

Federal Point of View

While many American fisheries remain under the haphazard control of individual States, let us look a little closer at the objectives of the industry from the federal point of view. Its spokesman is the Bureau of Commercial Fisheries of the U.S. Department of the Interior. The Bureau's long-range program, "Operation Trident," places emphasis on oceanographic research as a means of strengthening the commercial fishing industry and maintaining it in a healthy condition. Scientific research, it contends, can reduce the cost of locating and catching fish, thus making the product available in prime condition at reasonable prices; technological development can increase the efficiency of the industry at all levels.

Whether these objectives can be achieved at a cost consistent with the present economic and social structure of America's fishing industry are big questions. With a few outstanding exceptions, the whole industry is fragmental and economically weak. It lacks the capital to finance costly developmental projects, and it is struggling to compete against the products of lower-paid, heavily subsidized foreign fishermen. Our total landings have not increased in proportion to our population growth, although there are splendid fishery resources close to our coasts, which our fishermen could harvest if it were more profitable to do so. Our steady per capita consumption of seafood, about 10½ pounds per year, has been maintained by imports from many foreign countries. In 1963, for the first time in history, imports provided more than half the United States supply of fishery products.

Yet, according to *Ocean Science News,* a responsible Washington, D.C., newsletter: "Outside of the Navy's Anti-Submarine Warfare effort, there is no area of oceanographic endeavor with a greater applied technology market potential than that of the Interior Department's Bureau of Commercial Fisheries. Commercial fishing in the United States barely holds its own while that of the rest of the world rises sharply."

Gamut of Research Operations

Meanwhile the Bureau of Commercial Fisheries seeks to reverse this trend by running a gamut of oceanic research operations, though always, the Bureau points out, with the single objective of expanding the nation's fisheries potential. Modernization of old laboratories and construction of new ones continues, including: Seattle, Washington (oceanography), Beaufort, North Carolina (radiobiology), Milford, Connecticut (biology), Woods Hole, Massachussets (biology and aquarium), Ann Arbor, Michigan (biology), Miami, Florida (biology), and Washington, D.C. (biology, including the National Aquarium). The Bureau has 30 research vessels, with more abuilding. They operate in the eastern, central, and northern Pacific, the north and tropical Atlantic, the Caribbean, and the Gulf of Mexico, as well as up and down both coasts of the United States and in the Great Lakes. They are participating in the Indian Ocean Expedition, the Tropical Atlantic investigations, and in other Bureau programs.

In large measure the Bureau also cooperates with the Navy's needs, especially when the Navy wants detailed and continuing knowledge of fishes that may assist the service in predicting acoustical environment. The same data is needed to predict the density of sea life and migrations of certain species.

The Bureau of Commercial Fisheries is also examining close-in coastal and estuarian oceanography—the interplay between fresh and salt water in tidewater areas, shellfish culture, pest control in oyster beds, and the long-term effect of agricultural pesticides and persistent detergents that run off via the rivers. Ultimately the Bureau hopes to turn certain commercial fishing into an oceanic analogue of livestock raised ashore, where selected species are bred, raised, fed, herded, and harvested in a scientific manner—to take much of the luck, or rather lack of it, out of fishing. Concurrently, major efforts are being made to develop additional markets for fish and fish products, such things as fish protein concentrates or fish flour, and a new colorless, almost odorless fish-oil, now being investigated by the paint and pharmaceutical industries.

Shocking Way to Fish!

In terms of new fishing gear, the Bureau has several approaches, and the most dramatic are successful experiments with electrotrawling. This employs use of electrostatic fields in conjunction with trawl nets to (a) increase the yield, (b) select certain sizes, and (c) even differentiate between species. This effort is being intensified to determine the proper amounts of electrical currents and voltages for best results.

In addition, the Bureau is studying a research mesoscaphe, or medium-sized sub. This vehicle will be capable of a submerged speed of 20 knots with six weeks of uninterrupted underwater endurance, and three months total endurance at sea. Its depth will be 1,000 to 1,500 feet, and its length about 200 feet. Highly maneuverable, the vehicle will have a scientific crew of 4 to 8 and a working crew of 15 to 30. Sampling of currents, salinity, and electronics, and fish-tracking devices with underwater gear will be shared with other agencies, including the Geological Survey and the Bureau of Sport Fisheries.

The Bureau is not alone in planning underwater fisheries research. Experts from the Soviet Union are studying this new fishing technique by using a converted submarine to follow shoals of fish in the North Atlantic. By using midwater trawling in the areas where fish spend most of their time, between the surface and the seabed, the Soviets hope to learn a great deal more about why fish move at different speeds and in different places at different times of the year. By pinpointing such activities, much lost time in blind searching for large schools may be avoided.

Dr. A. I. Treschev, of the Institute of Marine Fisheries and Oceanography in Moscow, announced that a Soviet submarine the *Severyanka* has been converted into an underwater research ship that follows large shoals of herring, one of the most valuable of commercial fishes.

During the Fishery Gear Congress of the Food and Agricultural Organization, in 1963, midwater trawling was enthusiastically discussed. Hilmar Kristjonsson, chief of the FAO fishing-gear section, predicted that the technique "will open up entirely new fishing grounds." Midwater trawling is also highly regarded by biologists and conservationists. They believe it will help to reduce fishing pressure on the continental shelves of the world, where in some places stocks are being exhausted.

New fisheries are being developed at an ever-increasing rate around the world. The spectacular climb of fish meal production, using Peru's anchovetta, a fish whose value once came only indirectly through guano deposits, is an example. In 1957 Peru's production of fish meal totaled 64,000 tons; in 1963 it totaled 1,159,000 tons. During the past 10 years the United States has dropped behind Peru, Japan, Communist China, and the Soviet Union in total catch, and now ranks fifth. There is, of course, considerable doubt as to the accuracy of Red China's fishery statistics. Much of the traffic comes ashore in small junks, where the catch can only

MAKING FISHERIES PAY • 163

be estimated, but the need for it is heavy, and the total figures probably entitle the country to fourth place.

Here is the Scorecard

At any rate, the United States production of fish has been almost static for the past decade. In 1954, the United States domestic catch of all fish totaled 4,762 million pounds, whereas in 1963 it totaled 4,650 million pounds. As for edible fish, the production in the United States for 1954 totaled 2,705,000 pounds, and in 1963, 2,455,000 pounds. American fisheries provide direct employment for more than 200,000 citizens and indirect employment for over 300,000 others, many of them in communities with no other source of income. In cash, these fishermen landed a value of $378 million, $100 million under that of imports.

Yet the United States and its neighbor to the north share the richest concentration area of food fish in the world, now being exploited with superior equipment by fishing fleets of a dozen foreign countries. Today there are more than 500 modern Russian and Japanese fishing vessels within 40 miles of our coasts. Huge factory ships now pick up fish from trawlers and process it at sea, producing packaged fresh-frozen fish ready for market. The United States has no factory ships. Little wonder that during the past ten years the value of fishery imports to the United States has increased by more than $3 million, adding to our national deficit and drain on gold:

"Oceanic Engineering"

If we are to improve, or even maintain, our competitive position in harvesting the oceans' living resources we must not only modernize our fishing gear and tactics and expand our scientific research, but also we should utilize what might be called "oceanic engineering" in the following areas: (1) communication and navigation engineering, (2) search and detective engineering, (3) aggregation engineering, (4) harvest engineering, and (5) vessel engineering. Some of these activities may overlap with practical research, but this is to the general good in improving existing techniques of fish and shellfish harvesting, in developing radically new harvesting methods, in improving the efficiency of handling, processing, and storage of fish and shellfish at sea, and in devising new fishing vessel designs.

For example, effective fishing for pelagic (large, open-sea) fishes requires precision navigation, so reported John J. Supple, vice-president of the Maryland Tuna Corporation, at the Governor's Conference on the National Oceanographic Program, at Annapolis, Maryland, August 13, 1964. Fishermen must be able to return to particular areas where natural environmental conditions tend to aggregate various species of fishes. Current navigational devices used aboard fishing vessels are relatively accurate within 300 miles of shore where land station devices are available. However, over much of the open ocean, precision navigating by today's fishing vessels is impossible.

Present detecting systems for fish schools employ visual observations from shipboard and by aircraft and a variety of horizontal scanning and vertical sounding devices. It is problematical whether the effective range of such active "pinging" acoustical devices can be greatly extended. However, it is likely that better results can be achieved by refinements in existing acoustic devices. The development of FM Doppler acoustic devices would seem to offer promise in this area. Detection by listening to biologically emitted sound might also be worth investigation.

"Sniffers" For the Future

Future devices might include "sniffers," or mechanical devices capable of detecting extremely small quantities of substances given off by schools of fish. Fish schools, biologists believe, appear to leave "trails" similar to those of terrestrial animals. If a system could be devised to detect trails left by schools of fishes, and if directional gradients could be resolved, mechanical sniffers might be used to track the schools where they often pass by unnoticed.

Electrical currents have been used to collect fish which have been captured in seines, and some success has been achieved in the use of electricity to drive shrimp up from the ocean bed into the path of oncoming trawls. Electrical fields, air-bubble curtains, chemical curtains, light, and sound all appear to have some potential for aggregating marine fishes. German investigators have had some success in attracting fish by reproduction of certain biological sounds, and whales and porpoises can thus be called from distances as great as several miles.

Another approach which offers some promise is the use of chemical substances to attract or herd fish to designated areas. The high degree of olfactory perception, or "smell," in certain fishes and sharks implies that marine organisms may use this sensory system in detecting both prey and predators. Certain chemicals have been used by the Navy to repel sharks. If negative or positive responses can be achieved through small concentrations of substances, there is a likelihood that methods may be discovered for aggregating fish in the open ocean.

Netless Netting!

In the long run it might even be possible to develop systems which would forgo entirely the use of nets, the traditional means of capturing commercial fish. An example of this might be the further development of pump systems, now employed by the Russians in harvesting anchovy-like fishes. There is a parallel need for improvement in fishing vessel design, in order to use completely mechanical shipboard devices. Efforts might be directed toward improving deck layouts, as well as the best means for the handling, processing, and storage of fish aboard fishing vessels.

In 1951, the Bureau of Commercial Fisheries initiated the New England bluefin tuna project, to determine the feasibility of establishing a commercial tuna fishing and canning industry in New England, like the successful tuna fisheries off the Pacific coast. Much has been done since 1951, but it was only in the last few years (1961-1963) that a substantial tonnage of tuna was harvested. This included bluefin tuna and also skipjack tuna worth over $1 million at dockside. A fleet of 16 American vessels accounted for this catch in less than four months.

Scientists and commercial interests are becoming increasingly aware that tuna and other pelagic fish are not only abundant along the continental shelf at various times of the year, but also well out into the northwest Atlantic. The Woods Hole Oceanographic Institution has been investigating western Atlantic tuna since 1950. Its tagging program has been in effect for many years, as has also the tagging work done by the Marine Institute of Miami.

Wonders of Fish Flour

Another oceanic development that offers future expansion for industry is the processing of fish protein concentrate, sometimes referred to as fish flour. This product can be extracted from heretofore unused species of fish, often called scrap fish, or from the wastes of edible fish. The end product is an almost tasteless powder similar to flour. It can be transported and stored easily. It can be used to increase the protein content of an almost endless variety of dishes. It can be baked in bread. From Africa comes a report that it was employed, without detection, as a supplement to the native beer. It can be added to poultry and cattle feeds. Research is continuing on methods to develop this product more economically, on a large-scale commercial basis.

Whaling on Verge of Collapse

Most unusual of all commercial fisheries is the curious whaling industry of Antarctica. Although whales are mammals, not fish, they must be regarded as products of the sea when they are captured and processed for oil, meat, and bones. At any rate, there is little reason to argue about it, because the whaling industry is on the verge of collapse, according to the now almost defunct International Whaling Commission, which once kept track of the catches of whales and held them by quotas within economical and biological limits.

The world's major deep-sea whaling fleets in recent years have been operated in Antarctica, with only a few independent ships whaling off ports in the North Atlantic and the Pacific. The three principal Antarctic nations were Norway, the Soviet Union, and Japan. Norway and the Soviet Union had four fleets each, and Japan had seven. Each fleet was composed of about 18 vessels, including deep-sea trawlers and factory ships. Japan recently bought out the sole remaining fleet of the Netherlands, adding that country's 6 per cent quota of the world's catch to her own.

There seem to be many reasons why whaling has gone to pot, despite the efforts of the International Whaling Commission and the earnest pleas of marine biologists throughout the world. "The principal one," according to authoritative Mr. John Gulland, of the British Government's Fisheries Research Laboratory at Lewistock, England, "is that unlike other wild life resources, the whale belongs to no one and therefore it is in no one's direct interest to look after them." Asked if there was any positive evidence that the annual maximum quotas set in the past by the International Whaling Commission had been exceeded, Mr. Gulland said he had "a very strong suspicion" that whales had been caught out of the agreed season and also outside the agreed catching areas.

Next Season—Chaos?

To make matters worse, the International Whaling Commission failed to reach agreement on catch limitations during their annual meeting in Sandefjord, Norway, in June 1964. The result may be that whaling next season "is likely to continue virtually unrestricted." The blue whale, the biggest animal in the world, is believed to be close to extinction already. A near relative, the finwhale, has dropped from annual catches of 28,000 to less than half as many.

The situation is considered so acute that a council meeting of the United Nations Food and Agriculture Organization has been asked to discuss at some length the entire whaling industry, and, if possible, to submit proposals for a new whaling control board. If some stern means to limit catches in Antarctica is not worked out within the next year, whaling will soon cease to be economically possible for anyone, and an industry potentially worth $140 million a year will have been wrecked by greed and over-exploitation.

Perhaps at this sorry stage of the whales' decline, only the intervention of a large outside agency, such as the United Nations, could save them. While the United States is not directly concerned in the Antarctic whaling fleets, it has an indirect interest in some kind of an efficient whaling commission. A complete breakdown of international whaling might tempt nations to disregard other fisheries agreements of many kinds, such as those now existing in the Pacific and the Atlantic, in which the United States is vitally concerned.

But before the United States can speed the recovery of its fishery industry, antiquated laws must be reviewed, and revised if necessary. The federal government is already aware of much of the legislation that is badly needed. This legislation includes:

(1) The Vessel Replacement Act of 1964, designed to encourage modernization of our fishing fleets;
(2) The Fishery Research and Development Act of 1964, to encourage fishery research and development projects proposed by states, of which 42 produce fish commercially;
(3) The Bartlett Act, imposing strong penalties on invasion of our territorial waters by foreign fishing vessels;
(4) Legislation restoring historical public health services to vessel owners;
(5) Inclusion of surplus American fishery products in the Food for Peace Program, through amendment to the Foreign Assistance Act of 1963;
(6) Call for an International Conference on Conservation of Fisheries Resources, made in the unanimously adopted Senate Resolution 392, of the 87th Congress.

International commercial fishing has become such a mechanized big-haul business, especially as conducted by Russian and Japanese fleets, that several other nations have moved to extend their maritime jurisdiction from the traditional three miles (originally set as the range of an old, smooth-bore cannon shot) to anywhere from 12 to 200 miles.

As a result, a series of sharp international conflicts have reached the gunboat stage in several parts of the world. Britain and Iceland had a bloodless hassel over cod and haddock; France and Brazil exchanged harsh words over rock lobsters; and the United States and Ecuador tangled over tuna. In the latter case, 21 American boats were impounded briefly in Ecuador because they fished 13 miles offshore. Ecuador claims that its territorial waters extend 200 miles offshore. The United States recognizes only a three-mile territorial limit.

In 1960, an 87-nation conference tried, without success, to set a policy on maritime jurisdiction, including fisheries. The failure left an every-nation-for-itself situation. But the question will bob up again, to plague future maritime actions, until some country takes the initiative to set up and follow through an international agreement. Why not the

United States, through revival of the defunct Senate Resolution 392, of the 87th Congress, now gathering cobwebs in some forgotten pigeonhole?

CHAPTER X
GADGETS AND HARDWARE

MOST OF OUR FAVORITE FICTION of the sea dates back to the days of iron men and wooden ships. It is difficult to realize that our research battles with wind and wave today depend upon a somewhat different formula, reversing to strong steel ships—and tossing overboard completely the inevitable cliché about "wooden men." There is little use for giants among today's alert, versatile, and imaginative oceanographers. Brawn and muscle gangs have been replaced with a vast array of instruments and push buttons, with a few skilled men operating with them simultaneously on the surface as well as far below and high above the sea.

Unlike the prospector on land, who, for instance, may search for uranium ores alone with a pick and shovel, a magnifying glass, and a geiger counter, the seeker of the sea's mysteries must not only have an adequate ship under his feet, but must also have the fuel, food, special devices, and many other human and mechanical necessities to carry on his complicated work.

Not All Standardized

Some of this oceanic instrumentation has been standardized, but not all. Certain special equipment needed today is designed and built for limited use or single jobs. Quite a number of gadgets and needed hardware must be fashioned on board ship, while underway. This requires a small floating machine shop, because old baling wire and tar tape, the cure-all of the Model T, just won't do against the buffeting of rough waves, the corrosion of salt water, and the extremes of temperature to be found at sea.

However, much standardized gear and equipment has been put to general use. Some tools were devised many years ago, such as the Nansen bottle, invented by the celebrated Norwegian Arctic explorer Fridtjof Nansen for sampling water at different depths. Most live fish, plankton samples, and bottom sediments are hauled or otherwise obtained by nets, dredges, and coring tubes as they always were. The drift bottle, with its helpful message inside, still plays a part in the tracking of surface currents.

Difficult to Keep Up

As oceanography has developed into broader fields, the need for more and more instrumentation has expanded enormously. Like the Red Queen in *Through the Looking Glass*, one must run faster and faster to stay in the same place! As a result, even established oceanographers, especially those who must spend much time at sea, find difficulty in accepting many new intricate devices, even some hardware that is now more or less in general use: the precision graphic recorder, used for a variety of acoustical observations; the oxygen electrode for measuring dissolved oxygen; the electrical conductivity salinometer, which can replace chemical methods in determining the salinity of water; and scores of other sophisticated devices.

The need for accurate navigation, on, under, and over the sea, has suddenly increased the necessity of instruments for both merchant ships and warships. Much of the development of today's artificial ears and eyes of the sea, such as radar, sonar, and loran have come from oceanic research, finally distilled into applied technology and instruments.

Use of Satellites

Satellite navigation has already demonstrated its worth to the sea. Oceanographic data were transmitted in 1963, via *Syncom II* communications satellite, from the Bureau of Commercial Fisheries *R/V Geronimo*, operating in the southeast Atlantic, to the National Oceanographic Data Center in Washington, D.C.

Why was a satellite necessary? The *Geronimo*, participating in Equilant II (International Cooperative Investigations of the Tropical Atlantic), had collected data on temperature and salinity from depths down to 3,000 feet and needed to check this out quickly against data collected previously by other expeditions. It radioed the data to the U.S.N.S. *Kingsport,* the floating Syncom ground station anchored in Lagos, Nigeria, which transmitted it promptly to the satellite (NASA).

The latter relayed the data to the Lakehurst, New Jersey, ground station, which sent it via conventional ground lines to the Data Center. Here data were compared with available historical data from the five-degree square within which the reading had just been made. Deviations were sent back via the same route to the *Geronimo,* to correct several errors in the instruments or in observation techniques on board the ship.

Value of Such Work

The satellite experiment was more a test of communication speed rather than oceanographic data evaluation in this instance, but a quality control problem did develop from it. The oceanographic station data received from the *Geronimo* showed equivalent salinity deviations, which prompted oceanographers at the Data Center to accept the validity of the salinity values. As much malfunctioning might mean the discarding of many hours of work, the test proved valuable for such precise future experiments.

Once On a Spot Basis

Most observations made at sea have formerly been done on a spot basis, but now many oceanographic problems require continuous data. Instruments to meet this need are being developed; at the same time electronic computers are being used to process the huge amount of information involved.

New towed instruments for measuring water temperature at intervals down to 600 feet (limit of the bathythermograph, a well-known but slow instrument that records water temperature as a function of depth while towed by a vessel underway) are already in use. One device, a series of thermistors, has been lowered over the stern of the Woods Hole Oceanographic Institution's research vessel *Chain.* Towed behind the ship, this flexible broad band continuously reports temperatures at depths to 600 feet. It also has been used with hydrophones for acoustical studies, and with pitometers for measuring current sheer at different depths.

Focus of Modern Instrumentation

Most modern focus of gadgets and hardware is the new Oceanographic Instrumentation Center, Navy Yard Annex, Washington, D.C. Although it is listed as a Navy activity under the Naval Oceanographic Office, the Center cooperates with other government agencies, private industry, and the academic community (university marine centers and educational oceanic laboratories) to bring about general improvements and refinements in oceanic instrumentation. In brief, it is an effort to assure that technical data about the sea are precise, accurate, and nonduplicating, and available to everyone.

Since the early 1950s there has been an urgent need to bring together several scattered government offices aimed at kindred efforts and needs in instrumentation. Finally, in November 1962, the Navy assembled its own Oceanographic Office instrumentation division with a few other units at the present Center. It now has a staff of about 100 engineers, scientists, technicians, and support personnel. The Center contains engineering facilities for laboratory and contractual development, test and evaluation, as well as maintenance of instruments. Already it has worked out such new instrumentation as improved electronic bathythermographs, shipboard wave recorders, a shipboard survey system, submerged buoy systems, and sound velocimeters.

Shock and Vibration Tests

Modern test equipment at the Center includes pressure vessels, shock and vibration tests, tensile facilities, pressure and temperature tanks, and reversing thermometer calibration. Among unusual facilities there are a 60-foot clearwater instrument test tower and a small craft from the Navy Yard for testing in local waters.

After the usual bumps that follow the shakedown of a new organization, the Instrumentation Center is now expanding its program. Here are a few of the recent instruments and systems tested, or in process of being tested:

(1) Sea Surface Temperature Measurement Systems (SURTEMS). This system consists of a thermistor probe and a battery-operated indicator in an attempt to discover the most desirable method of measuring sea surface temperatures.
(2) Mechanical Bathythermograph (BT). As a result of reported operational faults of BT's in the field and laboratory, a study will check on their accuracy and the magnitude of their errors. From these studies, efforts will be made to improve the BT, still one of oceanography's most familiar and most valued devices.
(3) Airborne Radiation Thermometer (ART). Carried aboard an aircraft, ART measures the sea surface water temperature continuously by detecting sensitive infrared radiation from the sea surface. While it reads sea surface temperature directly on a meter and records it permanently on a strip-chart within the plane, ART has some bugs in correlation with other devices—hence it is being investigated.

Some In-house Support

The Center will also assist the Oceanographic Office's operating divisions in developing instruments and instrument systems through contract work and in-house efforts. Some recent developments include:

(1) Electronic Bathythermograph. This instrument is designed for installation aboard ship to measure water temperature as a function of depth and to provide a permanent record.
(2) Sound Velocimeter. The sound velocimeter is a recording system for: (a) sound-speed; (b) depth; and (c) temperature. With an operating range of 9,000 feet beneath the sea, the system provides for display of all three variables, and a printed record of any two variables.
(3) Shipboard Wave Height Recorder. This ingenious instrument is a sonic echoing device, consisting of a transducer package and a strip-chart recorder. The transducer package, mounted over the bow of a ship, contains the gyro-synchro motor to stabilize the package against the roll of the bow, a linear accelerometer to stabilize the package against the pitch of the ship, and a sonic sensor which measures the height of waves by means of reflected signals. The

system is designed to measure wave heights from ½ foot to 20 feet (40 feet total), periods from 2 to 25 seconds, and lengths from 20 to 2,500 feet.

Geophysical Problems

In addition to these varied activities, the Instrumentation Center also assists the operating divisions of the Navy in many oceanographic and marine geophysical problems. To select a few of these:

(1) Atlantic Underwater Test and Evaluation Center (AUTEC). This special program calls for a lot of sophisticated hardware, including sound-measuring instruments, hydrophone arrays, and shipboard instrumentation for the detection and collection of sound data; some developed in-house and others under contract. An acoustic instrumentation hut has been developed. It is completely self-contained, including the power plant and necessary electronics for monitoring hydrophone signals and recording on magnetic tape.

(2) Antisubmarine Warfare Environmental Prediction System (ASWEPS). New instrumentation has been developed for collecting data from many types of platform—including aircraft, ships, and buoys. In addition to ART, electronic BT and wave height sensors, already listed above, it has also added a 3-buoy array for measuring current direction, speed, and water temperature to depths from 50 to 188 feet. Also available is a NOMAD (unmanned weather station) buoy with 24-temperature and 3-pressure sensors strung along a 1,000-foot cable, which is able to send temperature and depth information to a central station at 6-hour intervals.

(3) Submarine Oceanographic Observation Program (SOOP). This uses submarines, rigged with devices and systems for the collection of oceanographic data. Instruments have been developed to collect data thus on sound velocity, temperature, salinity, depth, surface waves, and density.

A Shack on a Raft

Outside commercial organizations are being encouraged to set up instruments for their own work, or to sell to others. A contract to supply underwater beacons for MARS (Mobile Atlantic Range System) has been placed by Sperry Rand Corporation with The Bendix Corporation. These beacons are placed on the ocean floor and, in response to a surface-ship transmitted pulse, send back a similar signal to the ship. The system was developed for precise ship-positioning by vessels involved in missiles and space vehicle tracking.

A shack on a raft has been built by the Sparton Corporation as an effective yet low-cost answer to the need for a (relatively calm water) floating underwater acoustic laboratory. Consisting essentially of an 8- by 16-foot enclosure mounted on a platform supported by two 24-foot-long cylindrical tanks, the unit is used to conduct acoustical measurements involving free field response, sound levels, etc., as well as studies of neutrally buoyant devices, controls of the rate of descent of free-sinking bodies, and electronic instruments for taking oceanic measurements.

A portable salinity-temperature-conductivity salinometer, capable of measurements to depths of 300 feet, has been developed by Industrial Instruments, Inc. A highly compact instrument, it works simply by lowering an electrodeless cell into the water, bringing it up, and reading the data directly.

An Acoustic Command System

An acoustic command system has been developed by Ocean Research Equipment, Inc., Falmouth, Massachusetts, to provide an underwater command link for unattended buoy systems. A single command system has been delivered as part of a tide-measuring system for the Naval Oceanographic Office. A similar system is being built to employ 30 discrete commands and communicate with a multiple-buoy system.

One of the unique instruments devised by the Woods Hole Oceanographic Institution recently was a "stable oceanographic buoy." The tip of its 50-foot-high mast will move less than one degree in waves 10 feet high. Its purpose is to provide a stable platform in water too deep for the practical construction of seafloor-based towers. Woods Hole is studying the transfer of such properties as heat, moisture, and momentum between the ocean and the atmosphere "in a tradewind region at a depth where the waves do not feel the bottom." First the buoy is moored by cable to the bottom.

Then the main flotation tank of the buoy is cranked down to a mean depth of about 14 feet below the surface. This provides 5,000 pounds of excess buoyancy, which results in an extremely light mooring under high tension. Preliminary tests in 5-foot waves, moored at a depth of 100 fathoms, off Provincetown, Massachusetts, showed no discernable motion.

Still Much Standard Equipment

In spite of the exciting technological advances that have been made recently in oceanic instrumentation, much of the useful information about the sea we employ today in science and research has come from gadgets and hardware designed 25 years or more ago. Because many of these early measuring tools and platforms are still in general use today, particularly in various courses of instruction and in teaching young oceanographers, it is appropriate to mention them briefly:

(1) Earliest of all precise instruments was a simple device for measuring the temperature of the deep sea. It is known as the *deep sea reversing thermometer,* a mercury-and-glass contrivance that was developed in England in 1874.

(2) Water-sampling bottles date back even earlier (Hooke invented one in 1611), but the most famous is the one designed by Fridtjof Nansen in the late 19th century. It has a tube with valves at each end which is clamped to a wire lowered from a ship or a dock. When the top end of the bottle is released by a weight (messenger) that slides down the wire, the bottle reverses its position on the wire, sealing a sample of water and tripping a messenger for the next bottle down the wire. In this way a number of samples can be obtained during a "station," as a halt at sea for research is called.

(3) Many nets and associated devices have been employed to obtain plant and animal life from the sea. For plankton, there is the *Clarke Bumpus sampler,* a small net towed at slow speed. The *half-meter plankton net* and the *Hardy recorder* are also used for plankton and minute creatures. The *midwater trawl* collects larger biological specimens, using a depressing vane to keep the net at the required depth while being towed.

(4) A calibrated *hydrometer* measures the density of seawater, which is related to salinity. The best means

of measuring the salinity of seawater is to determine its chlorinity (salt). Because there is a fixed relationship between the various chemical components of seawater, analysis may be checked with a uniform seawater sample known as *Copenhagen standard seawater*, a media used by oceanographers throughout the world.

(5) Marine geology is represented by many kinds of technical devices used to obtain cores, grabs, or dredges from the ocean bottom. Best known of coring instruments are the *Phloger, Ewing, and Kullenberg corers*, which pierce the mud bottom with tubes weighted at the top and also have nose pieces which retain the material.

Orange Peel and Clamshell

(6) For sea bottom samplers there are orange peels, clamshells snappers, and various kinds of dredges. The *orange peel* has four jaws, like a peeled quartered orange, and digs by gravity. The *clamshell snapper* has two jaws which are spring-loaded to obtain material. *Bottom dredges* gain specimens from boxes, open at one side and closed by bars at the opposite side so as to collect rocks.

(7) Not all marine geology is concerned with the collection of tangible material. A prime need is bottom topography, called bathymetry, for which an *echo sounder* or an *oscillograph* is needed. Echo sounders transmit a sonic pulse to the bottom and obtains its echo, the time interval being a function of the depth to the bottom. An oscillograph employs an explosive charge, recording the sonic returns. More powerful than an echo sounder, the oscillograph may also penetrate the surface mud and underlying layers of sediment, thus not giving a true top layer. The instrument picking up the sound underwater is the *hydrophone*, a form of microphone.

Geophysical Devices

(8) Some mention should be made of the close kinship of marine gravity and magnetics with the geological properties of the sea. The *gravity meter*, or gravimeter, and the *Vening Meinesz pendulum* are two of these geophysical devices for measuring gravity. They should not be confused with other instruments

for taking magnetic measurements in the ocean, such as the *marine magnetometer*.

(9) Meteorology or the study of weather at sea requires a number of unusual instruments, in addition to visual observations. The *anemometer* measures wind speed and direction; the *hygrometer* or a *sling psychrometer* notes humidity; the *barometer* measures atmospheric pressure; and the *recording pyrheliometer* indicates the heat budget between the atmosphere and the ocean.

(10) Perhaps the easiest and most widely used tool of the sea is the *drift bottle*, which is released from a ship or along the shore and later retrieved. A message within the bottle indicates the data desired. Sometimes there is a card that offers a small reward for finders.

(11) Almost as simple was the first measurement of sea temperature by a *bucket thermometer*. Of deep sea temperature instruments in use today there are two types: One is sheltered from pressure or *protected*; the other is the *unprotected thermometer*.

(12) The most famous *temperature-measuring* instrument is the *bathythermograph*, or the *BT*, as it is known by oceanographers everywhere. For depths to 600 feet, it can be towed at 12 knots to carry the largest volume of oceanographic temperature data now available, although electrical thermometers are increasing in importance as oceanographic instruments.

(13) A *sound velocimeter* has replaced the former method of determining the velocity of sound in seawater by computing it from temperature and salinity. Sound velocity is now measured by an instrument that transmits a sound signal over a fixed path length. Time required to travel from the transmitter to the receiver is a measure of the sound velocity.

The Secchi Disc

(14) Another simple gadget, but not useful under all conditions, is the *Secchi disc*, by which water depths have been measured for many years. A rope or line lowers a white or a black disc into the sea until it is no longer visible. The depth at this point is measured. Now we have more accurate devices, such as the *hydrophotometer water clarity meter* and the *bathyphotometer*, which have photoelectric cells or

photomultiplier tubes. One is so sensitive that it can record light from ambient or natural sources, such as luminescent animal life.

(15) Because depth is important to almost all measurements made in the sea, and because it is varied by the fact that sea pressure increases at a uniform rate with depth, many measuring instruments have been devised to meet various situations. Among them is a Bourdon tube, connected to a variable resistor—a *pressure potentiometer*. Another is the *strain gage*, an electromechanical device; and the most recent—a *vibrating wire pressure gage*, which consists of a fine wire stretched in a magnetic field.

(16) In locating an oceanographic sample within the sea, three coordinates are important. Depth is one, and the other two are latitude and longitude. The latter two are determined at sea by positioning systems, such as: *shoran* (*sho*rt *ra*nge *n*avigation), *lorac* (*lo*ng *ra*nge *ac*curacy), and *loran* (*lo*ng *ra*nge *n*avigation). These differ chiefly in the type of transmission, the method of generating the signal, and the frequency used.

(17) The *Eckman current meter*, another old-timer, consists of a simple device to determine the number of revolutions made in an accurately timed interval.

Challenge Ahead

What about the future of instrumentation? Even what is already known and planned for the next decade indicates that the need for more oceanographic research is formidable. Future basic science of the sea must work even closer with technology and engineering, with a dash of imagination and a bit of calculated risk, if the job ahead is to be done.

Note this quote: "The shortage of instruments not only retards the increase in the scope of oceanographic research but . . . leads to the fact that the best survey fleet in the world, whose building and equipment has cost hundreds of millions . . . is not utilized to its full."

Thus reads a passage in a recent bulletin of the Oceanographic Commission of the Academy of Sciences. Of the United States? *No, of the Soviet Union!*

"It seems," says Don Groves, of the National Academy of Sciences (USA), "that the United States government and oceanographic planners are not completely alone in their feeling that the need for new and improved oceanographic survey instruments is one of today's most pressing requirements for the advancement of our national welfare in a variety of areas, military and civilian."

The Needs in Essence

Rear Admiral L. D. Coates, former Chief of U.S. Naval Research, recently pointed up the importance of understanding such hydrospheric studies as: ocean currents (surface and subsurface), ocean temperatures and densities, ocean salinity, chemistry and depths, sediment structure and ocean floor topography and geology, marine life, tide and wave motion, and meteorological information.

There is a lot of bread with not much butter to spread on it under existing appropriations. Oceanographers find it difficult to keep step with instrumentation costs for two major reasons:

(1) Such facilities must be used in a harsh environment (seawater is one of the most corrosive liquids known to man). They demand the utmost of a designer's skill because temperatures must be correct to the nearest .01 degree Celsius (formerly Centigrade), and salinity must have even greater precision. Other instruments, such as thermal probes to measure heat flow through the sediments at the bottom, depth recorders, sonic probes, plankton collectors, and audiovisual devices for fish observations and survey have extreme demands on their quality.

(2) The second reason why oceanographers may continue to have difficulty in keeping up with the instrumentation parade might be called inherent. That is, a demand for high-quality, expensive work is coupled with little demand for quantity. As a result, there has been little incentive for heavy investment in development by those industries most competent to advance the state of the art.

Exceptions to the Rule

Consequently, most oceanic instruments have been originally designed and manufactured in only such quantities as were needed by the oceanographers themselves, or by technicians in small marine laboratory workshops. The familiar Nansen bottle, still in wide use after 50 years, the bathythermograph, and the Ekman current meter are among the few exceptions that can be built elsewhere in quantity.

Naval Research Reviews, a reliable publication of the Office of Naval Research, predicted in 1963:

> "Development during these next ten years is expected to emphasize increased speed and efficiency of standard measurements, rather than the creation of devices for obtaining new types of information.
>
> "In addition to automating many of the shipboard procedures now being carried out tediously by hand, the Navy, Coast and Geodetic Survey, Bureau of Commercial Fisheries, Coast Guard and the Weather Bureau are seeking automated fixed stations for sensing and transmitting oceanographic data remotely on a routine basis.
>
> "Instrumentation for marine biology has lagged even farther behind than that for other aspects of marine science, and . . . efforts will be made to develop more satisfactory plankton recorders, sampling gear, and underwater camera and television equipment. A so-called 'parameter follower' is being sought by several agencies. This device, intended to be towed or self-propelled, would sense a given concentration of one parameter and remain within it while recording variations in others. It is expected to be particularly useful in fish migration studies, simulating some of the important behavior patterns of migrating fish.
>
> "Moored buoys, with strings of current meters for obtaining extended records at a given point, have been in use for several years. The present models require retrieval in order to obtain the data, and this has proved both time consuming and unreliable. Developing moored buoy systems to accomodate a variety of instruments and telemeter data and then sent (by radio) to shore stations, aircraft, or satellites has therefore become an attractive possibility."

The Navy expects to carry about three-fifths of the United States total for the instrumentation program, reflecting the massive effort for defense needs. The remaining two-fifths will be divided among the Bureau of Commercial Fisheries, Geological Survey, Bureau of Mines, Coast Guard, Weather Bureau, and Coast and Geodetic Survey. There will be an increasing exchange of information among these agencies and a central file of instrumentation data at the National Oceanographic Data Center, and the joint agency use of the

Navy's new Oceanographic Instrumentation Center, at the Navy Yard Annex, in Washington, D.C., as well as noting the new Smithsonian Oceanographic Sorting Center, also at the Navy Yard Annex.

CHAPTER XI

OCEANIC DEFENSE PROBLEMS

As a rule, oceanographers, like other scientists dedicated to the study of basic truths, do not like to mix military aspects with their work. But today marine research and marine warfare are so interrelated that the civilian scientist must accept certain national responsibilities and withhold some of his findings as secret or classified. Guardian of the USA's safety in the ocean domain is the U.S. Navy, which invests far more money in oceanography than does any other organization, and especially so in the Navy's submarine and antisubmarine programs.

This is in keeping with the Navy's traditional role of defending the United States against would-be invaders. Until recent years such defense was aimed at foreign surface vessels. Now with the development of modern submarines, new strategies in defense and offense operations must be devised. Modern techniques must enable us not only to find and destroy enemy submarines that can cruise for great distances and for days beneath the surface, but also to devise ways to protect our own submarines from being demolished by an alien power.

Latent Sea Threat

While the Free World, led by the United States, wants to remain at peace with the countries behind the Iron and Bamboo Curtains, the Soviet Union must continue to be considered, for all practical purposes, as the most powerful potential opponent of the United States. China has not yet developed as a marine force, but the U.S.S.R. exists as a latent sea threat of increasing strength, both militarily and scientifically.

Unlike the carrier task forces that symbolize the various fleets of the Free World, the Soviet Navy has militarily concentrated at sea on submarines, and now has the largest submarine force in the world. It is quite obvious that the Soviet Union has not assembled this immense undersea fleet, some 400 conventional boats and an indeterminate number (possibly a dozen) of nuclear craft, simply to defend its own few seaports, most of which lie well inland or are icebound much of the year. It may be assumed, therefore, that the U.S.S.R.'s submarines are intended almost entirely for offensive operations, such as launching pads for missiles along the exposed shorelines of the Free World, or as commerce raiders along essential sea lanes critically needed for economic and military production support, or for sowing mine fields, or even for landing and retrieving of special troops used for demolition, intelligence, and planted pollution.

Priority to ASW

That the United States is fully aware of the situation is indicated by the high priority recently given by the Congress and the Pentagon to the development of antisubmarine warfare (ASW) research. A new Secretary of the Navy in 1964 was asked what subject he would like to tackle first. "Please brief me on antisubmarine warfare," he replied. The Navy has announced also that henceforth a vice admiral will head up a special ASW division, the highest rank yet assigned for the subject. The title will be backed up with plenty of Navy authority, and fortified by Congressional appropriations which have jumped from $248 million in 1961 to $386 million in fiscal 1965. In the face of severe cuts made in other defense spending recently, it is significant that ASW's funds, compared with the total for Navy research, development, test, and evaluation, jumped from 18 per cent in 1961 to 27 per cent in 1965.

Much remains to be done, both defensively and offensively, at sea. Naval strategy under water is especially complicated not only because the human eye cannot penetrate the dark depths of the ocean but also because even the most modern sounding devices are far from accurate. The best we have achieved for both surface vessels and submarines is equipment called sonar, which sends out sound waves, or "pings," through the water. When these pings strike an object under the water they rebound to the sending ship. From the known speed of the sound waves and the time required for them to travel outward and return, we generally can locate a lurking enemy.

Signals Erratic

Sonar devices, however, are limited in their usefulness, not because the machinery is faulty but because of the complex nature of the sea. Many factors, such as sudden changes in salt content, or the water's temperature, or the movement of currents, may throw off sonar beams. Even marine animals, such as whales and deep scattering layers of marine life, sometimes make acoustic signals erratic, hence unreliable. The comparative short range of sonar affords protection to submarines trying to *escape detection* in the open sea.

In 1959 the Committee on Oceanography of the National Academy of Science stated: "The problems involved in military operations in the sea are enormous. We will not be able to navigate under the oceans with adequate precision until our knowledge is greatly expanded. Nor will we be able to detect submerged submarines efficiently unless we learn far more about the ocean depths than we now know."

The ocean sciences have had and will continue to play a leading role in the elusive "breakthrough" the Free World must achieve to protect its shores from undersea enemies. The defensive battle-front for the U.S.A. alone now includes not only the continental United States, but also two outlying states, Alaska and Hawaii, as well as such other commitments as Puerto Rico, the Canal Zone, Guantanamo, the Virgin Islands, Guam, Samoa, the Mandated Territories of the Pacific, and other small isolated islands and shoals. Added together this constitutes the longest inhabited coastline of any nation on earth.

Not One-Sided

Fortunately, the submarine problem is not one-sided. As a counter check, the United States and its allies have the Polaris-firing nuclear submarine, now deployed to reach 35 to

40 million people in the Communist land mass. The new Polaris A-3 missile, launched at sea, now has a range of 2,500 nautical miles. Russia's present range of missiles is believed to be only about 400 miles, but the Soviets may consider this sufficient because such missiles from submarines would reach many of our major cities, which lie upon or very near exposed coasts.

However considered, therefore, oceanography and other marine research have become sciences of extreme strategic importance. Today's submarines are capable of operating at such depths and ranges that much more knowledge of the sea floor is vital. These call for modern oceanic charts, contour maps, and special marine computers. Sonar equipment needs for its operations additional sound and temperature data. Amphibious landing losses in World War II were increased by heavy surf. A better scientific knowledge of currents would have helped in safer planning operations. Ship routing, disposal of waste at sea, storms, etc., are also influenced by wave and current information. Oceanographers today use a host of scientific instruments, such as bathythermographs to measure temperature and modern echo sounders—all of them of prime need for the military.

Attacker Sub Ahead

To the average person, a submarine is a dangerous place to live, from the nature of things, and an attack or aggressor submarine must be the most dangerous and difficult of all military jobs. But strange vicissitudes confront those who must *defend* themselves from submarine attacks. Unfortunately, the United States must play both sides of this undersea fence, with enemy submarines attacking and submarines of our own attempting to halt them, and then reversing the game.

Strange as it may seem to the layman, the attacker has a better chance of success today than the forces arrayed against him. This is because the seas are so big, compared with the few ships and instruments that can be deployed against attacking submarines. The attacker, more often than not, may complete his mission and return unscathed. Until we gain a great deal more about the whole sea from top to bottom, a stupendous task that will require many years, the submarine must be able to "see" yet be "unseen"—a neat trick indeed!

ASW Gap Closing?

So the submarine *aggressor* remains still ahead of the submarine *defender,* although experts admit that the antisubmarine warfare gap has been closing somewhat as a result of new developments and the increasing capability of ASW staffs and operations. Much of this work must remain classified, or secret, such as certain parts of the Deep Submergence Systems Review Group, launched shortly after the U.S.S. *Thresher* disaster, to delve deeper into sea operations, and the Anti-Submarine Advisory Committee Report, which sizes up our 1964 status in submarine warfare. But enough has been announced to the public to explain why every naval officer, oceanographer, and marine technician should roll up their collective sleeves, and step up ASW efforts all around. The concluding remarks of the *Report, Department of Defense Appropriation Bill* 1965, give guidance as well as a solemn warning:

> The Committee does not want to exhibit pessimism, but does want to call attention to the difficulties inherent in anti-submarine warfare. Three distinct problems exist: location of submerged objects, classification of unknown objects, and the destruction of enemy submarines. At the present time the weapons which could destroy enemy submarines have a range exceeding that of the location and classification equipment. Thus the positive location and classification of hostile submarines is an area requiring greater emphasis.

Polaris Proved a Principle

On a hot summer day off the coast of Florida, a submerged submarine moved slowly into position. Minutes later awed spectators watched a geyser of water spurt from the Atlantic's calm surface. A gleaming white-and-black missile leaped into the air and seemingly hung suspended for a moment before its engine barked into life. Then, trailing a thin white track of smoke, the missile roared into the blue sky and landed 14 minutes later "on target" over 1,000 miles away.

Thus was demonstrated for the first time the Polaris Fleet Ballistic Missile weapon system, July 20, 1960. Here was dramatic proof that missiles could be launched successfully from under water against a distant target. The accomplishment held two sobering messages:

(1) The United States has the ability to retaliate from the safety of the ocean on an aggressor nation.
(2) Potential enemies soon will be able to launch missiles from under water against American targets, now that they have been shown that the system works in principle.

No Panacea Available

The need for more effective submarine countermeasures remains critical. As a recent Chief of Naval Operations (Admiral George W. Anderson) put it: "We must be able to detect and kill *Polaris*-type submarines which might be deployed against us to launch a surprise attack. We see no major breakthrough on the horizon for antisubmarine warfare, no panacea to solve our problems. Detecting and destroying underwater ships remains a very, very difficult problem."

In protecting American shores from attack, and millions of tons of this nation's international waterborne commerce, United States ASW forces must not only be able to detect other submarines and determine their positions, but they must also be *certain* whether they are friends or foes, and then have the ability to "kill" the enemy first if the situation warrants it. This calls for not only a host of equipment or "hardware," but makes even more demands upon the ocean sciences, particularly below the surface.

Take the hardware first. To deal effectively with even our present threat, the U.S. Navy uses modern submarine-hunting airplanes, drone and manned ASW helicopters, destroyer-launched ASW rockets, destroyer and submarine-launched torpedoes, mines and other depth charges, submarine-launched ASW rockets, and SUBROC. As tomorrow's problems become tougher, the enemy's submarines will develop electronic gear that will be able to detect our ASW forces more easily and certainly.

Fire Control Computers

Meanwhile, of course, America will not be standing still. Technicians of the United States are designing new precision ASW equipment, such as fire control computers, torpedo guidance systems, and underwater weapon systems simulators, and other weapon devices still cloaked in secrecy. Test tanks are being employed to study various submerged components, and shielded rooms make extremely sensitive electromagnetic measurements.

The submarine defender today faces future problems that will evolve from many new concepts of undersea attack, some of American origin. An aircraft in warfare must climb higher to gain an advantage; so the submarine, defensive or offensive, will have to dive lower to win. For the submarine this may call for a startling new approach in the vehicle itself. Until now, the submarine has had to have buoyancy, so that it could hover motionless in the water to stalk its prey or could float to the surface in case its engines failed. To go deeper and to gain more speed in the depths, however, the submarine may have to abandon its cherished buoyancy. With negative buoyancy such craft would have to be in motion all of the time, or it would sink like a rock.

Not a New Idea

The idea is not a new one; aircraft faced a similar problem when the floating dirigible was replaced by the dynamically supported airplane. A submarine with negative buoyancy would perforce be a constant prowler or an attacker, and would be on the move from the time it left port until the motors are cut off in a dry or floating dock at the end of a voyage. Modern efforts to make submarine machinery more nearly silent are being tested, but the whole concept of a ship that must move to live at sea is such a wrench on the credulity of established mariners that much study naturally confronts it.

If submarines must go deeper and swifter, much more research must be done on the accurate mapping of the ocean bottom. Modern echo-sounders show that the sea floor is vastly different from any past conceptions. Limited work already completed shows that its contours may be even more varied than those on dry land. In any event, the bottom is not relatively flat and uneventful, as it once was thought to be. Occasionally a survey vessel will discover an underwater peak or pinnacle of rock which has been passed over by surface ships but which would destroy a rapid-moving submarine.

Maps from Stereo Cameras

For the past several years the U.S. Coast and Geodetic Survey has been experimenting with ocean floor mapping by means of stereo cameras. In 1960 the Oceanographic Office of the Navy began development of an underwater stereo camera system capable of taking photos suitable for photogrammetric measurements and subsequent studies of microrelief of the ocean bottom. (Designed by H. E. Edgerton, famous undersea photographer, it consists of two cameras mounted on a 12-foot frame, two electronic light sources, and a sonar pinger which enables the winch operator to maintain the camera-to-bottom distance required for sharp focus.

In operation, the stereo camera system is controlled by a timing device which delays the start of photography until the cameras (each loaded with either color or monochrome film) are lowered to the desired depth. When activated, the cameras can take photos continuously for about two hours, while being towed by the ship.

A Coast and Geodetic Survey process, known as "microcontouring of the ocean floor," has a three-dimensional camera view. It produces a detailed map sufficient to show the depth of minute crevices, the height of sand ripples, and even the pockmarks of worm holes. In 1962, aided by more powerful lighting, Coast and Geodetic Survey cameras were activated 25 feet above the ocean bottom, photographing more than 400 square feet at a time.

Ooze As a Trap

Undersea mountains or crags are not the only menace to the deep-ranging submarine. Patches of ooze, similar in action to quicksand ashore, cover large areas of the ocean floor. If a submarine were to land on such an area, it might sink into the muck and be unable to get loose. Although such ooze locations can be spotted by sonic warning devices, ordinary sonar might not be a reliable aid, since ooze sometimes absorbs sound and reflects it back from layers lower down in the ooze. The problem has been partially solved by the use of the sonoprobe, devised by an oil company. This device uses low-frequency sound, rather than high-frequency sonar, to probe underlying sediments, and usually gives a true bottom because of its frequency in different types of oozes, and its speed through water.

The overall use of underwater sound is still far more an art than a science, with devices that rely on intuition and educated guesswork. Temperature and salinity play hob with ordinary sonars, which are still the military's best means of detecting undersea objects. Quick changes in temperature have great effect on sonar sighting, because water temperature changes affect the water's salinity, which, in turn, affects how fast the sound waves may travel through the water. In the end there may be nothing but a dim signal that appears to be farther away than it is, or is not discernable between a metallic or nonmetallic body.

Porpoises With a Purpose

Acoustic detection, while it remains our primary means of discovering the presence of submerged submarines, has not eliminated attempts to use underwater radar and other means of attaining targets. Scientists are pessimistic about the detection of radar operations under water, because of the laws of physics, and declare that any reported radar detections are accidental. Research, however, goes on, and one of the interesting aspects is the use of live porpoises, with studies being made of their echo-ranging characteristics.

While sonar may not be replaced for many years, a supplementary device shows promise. It is called MAD (Magnetic Anomaly Detector), and it is carried by ASW planes, helicopters, and blimps. It acts like a large magnet—sensing changes in the earth's magnetic field, with a range less than sonar. Its chief use is in spotting a distant or deep-water enemy submarine and then sending the word to an ASW destroyer or submarine to close in with sonar contact. In MAD's favor too, is the fact that it won't pick up fish, which are nonmetallic and have no effect on the earth's magnetic field.

Another vexing problem that oceanographers have not yet

solved for themselves or for the military is the thermocline, a thin boundary of water or layer that divides the surface waters from the main part of the ocean. These cooler waters below the warm surface waters are located 10 feet or more below the ocean surface. They occur in widely varying fashion, but whenever a thermocline takes place, sonar ranges must be reworked to meet the new conditions. The presence of a thermocline may give a false bottom or otherwise affect submarine communications and detection.

Bottom-bounce!

Bottom-bounce and convergence zone methods of sonar operations, plus variable depth sonars, have been suggested by Naval technicians as a means of improving several varied ASW problems. Passive detection methods may give the "missing link" of range, which has been limited to "bearing only."

Navy scientists at the U.S. Naval Ordnance Laboratory have determined that an explosive charge is a better source of sound than electrical transducers presently employed in certain studies of sound transmission under the sea. The primary purpose of this project is to learn more about how to predict the obscuring effect of back-scattering by the ocean floor on sonar signals.

Navy scientists have also completed the first phase of a plan to send deep-water transmissions of sound across the Atlantic Ocean. The project is expected to prove useful for improving present submarine detection and underwater communication systems, which use the sea's sound velocity channel as a medium of sound transmission. This is a natural sound track in which underwater sound waves are confined because of the interacting effects of the sea's temperature and density. Once confined to this track, sound produced at any output level tends to be refracted to the level of minimum speed and remain there. This enables it to travel great distances with relatively little decrease in intensity.

Sound under the Sea

During the data-collection phase of the project, a pair of explosive charges were dropped every 100 miles across the Atlantic and the resulting sounds were recorded with underwater hydrophones located along the sound track's axis near Bermuda. It was found that at a depth of about 4,000 feet, sea temperatures and density (the speed of sound in water increases with temperature and decreases with pressure) are best to trap sound waves for long-distance transmission throughout the whole ocean.

Nautical charting and the source of information on earthquakes, on the magnetic forces that affect the compass and the radio, on the pull of gravity which can deflect the surveyor's plumb bob, and on geodetic points for control of engineering projects and land surveys—all these play a part in many oceanic defense problems.

Although many landlubbers may not know it, the Coast Survey has a scientific fleet of its own—a total of 16 ships, manned by a total of 500 crewmen and 200 officers. The two major bases are at Norfolk and Seattle.

The Coast Survey produces charts of the United States primarily in the support of non-military needs; the Naval Oceanographic Office covers the rest of the world's charts in support of the U. S. military.

Motto: "Always Ready!"

In peacetime the Coast Guard operates in the Treasury Department, yet it is always ready to function as a specialized armed service in the Navy. Military oceanographic requirements are included and discussed in Navy plans, and these include Coast Guard contributions in such secret areas as ASW, convoys, and actual wartime operations.

Oceanography is a natural interest of the Coast Guard, which has taken part in International Ice Patrol work since 1914, and for nearly a hundred years kept the Bering Sea Patrol. In 1961 the Congress gave the Coast Guard much greater authority in oceanographic research and made the Coast Guard a member of the Interagency Committee on Oceanography (ICO), created in 1960 to coordinate the oceanographic activities of various government agencies in developing a national program.

The Coast Guard participates in seven oceanic activities of the program—along with the Corps of Engineers (Army), Coast and Geodetic Survey, and the Navy—as follows: ocean-wide surveys, inshore surveys, ocean waves and swell, icebergs and icebound areas, radioactivity in the sea, oil pollution of navigable waters, and military oceanography.

Not Nearly Enough

It must be obvious by these few examples of oceanic defense problems, and of the agencies that are allied with the military in safeguarding our future, that the sea is an unbelievably difficult medium in which to work. One of the top officials at the Pentagon frankly admits that we do not yet have nearly enough oceanographic knowledge to begin to do our military tasks at sea. It is estimated that fewer than two-tenths of one per cent of the 300,000 senior scientists in this country work on marine matters. Dr. Harrison Brown, of California Institute of Technology, told the Senate: "Nobody knows how to go about monitoring nuclear subs. ASW is, I believe, the gravest, most difficult problem we face in the military field."

Resolved to its simplest terms—under the sea we are not yet able to hit what we aim at! Although American genius can accurately land a satellite on the moon, or guide a far-off probe close to Venus, we cannot be sure of spotting an undersea target from a submarine a mile away. Why, after so many years of research, should this be?

CHAPTER XII

A GLIMPSE INTO THE FUTURE

SO MUCH FOR THE *past* and the *present* of oceanography. Now let us turn with vigor toward the *future*. First of all, suppose we bypass some of the crystal gazing, rosy pipe dreams, the far-fetched Buck Rogers hardware, and the so-called "cloud nine" treatment now in vogue. Of these fabrications we have had rather more than our share lately in television, radio, newspapers, magazines, and books.

No, the actual needs confronting the immediate future of oceanography are obviously of sterner stuff, and they are right at hand—and urgent. This does not mean that they are dull or unimaginative, but in essence they call for just as much perspiration as inspiration; action as dreams. Inspiration, dreams, and imagination will play their parts too; but let's face it, if oceanography is to carry out the important jobs it seems ordained to do for the world in general, the nation in particular, and for people as individuals, it must have a greater grasp of its present role. It must somehow acquire and teach more oceanic talent, and especially it must obtain regular sources of money—from private industry, from foundations, and from government.

Facing Enemies from Within

Oceanography, too, must face its enemies from within; the timid souls who have watched with concern as oceanography expands and spreads its activities into allied but necessary fields. "This *really* isn't oceanography," they protest, not realizing that what constitutes oceanography by law has not yet been defined by the Congress of the United States—although Congress should do so. Other alarmists see increasing danger in the federal support of oceanographic research, which climbed from $24 million in the fiscal year 1958 to $124 million in 1963—not a very large sum when you consider the billions being spent on space projects. They point out, for instance, that the petroleum industries along the continental shelves do most of their own oceanic research with their own funds. Why not follow this example?

But as you study the enormous concept of the sea, you find that few patterns fit many situations, and some fit none. Some things are badly needed and must be done, although they are not financially profitable. It is impossible to put dollar values, private or government, on many vital oceanographic research requirements, and particularly on those for national defense. Although the U.S. Navy's program for oceanography is only a tiny segment of the total Navy expenditures (less than one per cent), nearly half of the total federal expenditures for the marine sciences comes from the Navy. This appears to be little or big, depending on the way you look at it. Much military research, particularly in submarine warfare and antisubmarine warfare, is difficult to evaluate because it must necessarily be done under security wraps.

Similarly, it is hard to arrive at dollar values on certain human needs, or at many political (in the broadest sense) oceanic equations; such as, for instance, greater understanding and use of the open seas and their depths, or the benefits to be derived from national prestige in "showing the flag" in foreign ports, or the intangible profits obtained from international understanding and comity overseas.

Science Suddenly Caught up with Us

Why are such incorporeal matters so important today and tomorrow? Because *science as a whole* has suddenly caught up with us, both in dollars and in sense. The federal budget for overall research and development including the requirements for outer space, inner space (sea), nuclear devices, etc., has been *growing much faster than the rate for the gross national product*, yet it is still only about 3 per cent of the gross national product.

However, it might be a good time for a thorough reappraisal, or stock-taking, as they say in the grocery store. As a yardstick, let us attempt to evaluate, in economic terms, what *benefits* may be expected from a given *expenditure of funds* on scientific research and development. Because this enormous problem goes far beyond the scope of this book, let us pinpoint on the growing portion devoted to oceanography.

Fortunately, we have at hand some fresh information (December 1964) from *Economic Benefits from Oceanographic Research,* a special report of the Committee on Oceanography, National Academy of Sciences–National Research Council. It estimates that "a continuing national investment in oceanography of approximately $165 million a year (not counting the part for national defense) will be an essential component in bringing about savings of nearly $3 billion a year, plus added annual production worth almost as much."

How can this tasty plum be explained? The Committee's chairman, Dr. Milner B. Schaeffer, of Scripps Institution of Oceanography, places the federal budget for oceanographic research at about $138 million in fiscal 1965. Projected budgets, shown in ICO Pamphlet No. 10, of June 1963, indicates an annual average growth of about 10 to 11 per cent, reaching some $350 million in fiscal 1972. By 1980, the long-range benefits of oceanography in the United States may thus total $6 billion a year!

Report Really Conservative

Actually the new report (Publication 1228) may be considered somewhat conservative, because it concerns itself primarily with *ocean sciences*—with only a secondary interest in *ocean engineering*. Cargo submarines are mentioned only briefly; tourist submarines, not at all. "Improved recreational facilities" get a $2 billion-a-year benefits total, but again little reference is made directly to undersea recreation—amateur subs, "aquotels," treasure hunting, etc.

Specifically, the document sees these possible benefits (given in millions per year) for some of the major or most greatly needed civilian oceanographic activities: increased fisheries production, $555 (10 to 15 years hence); mining of manganese, phosphorite, and placer deposits, $190 (10 years); lower shipping costs, $890 (10 to 15 years); improved long-range weather forecasts through better understanding of air-sea interaction, $2,000 (15 years); near-shore sewage disposal, $80; etc.

There are more statistics in Table 1 of the report, but these are typical examples. The primary purpose is to reveal economic benefits resulting from oceanographic research. They are two kinds: (1) annual savings in cost of goods and services, and (2) increases in production. While perhaps one may argue with the form of the report and some of its specific figures and projections, one cannot argue with its basic theme: *sufficient effort* applied in the exploration and understanding of the ocean can bring us great benefits; *insufficient effort* could bring us many and great catastrophes, especially in undersea warfare and antisubmarine warfare, which lean heavily on many still unsolved problems, some of them critical, that oceanography alone can solve.

One thing that is obvious is that such uncomplicated use of the sea as surface transportation does need more oceanic research (weather forecasting) to determine the best currents and to avoid storms, so that ships may save time and money through shorter and safer voyages.

Such speed-ups by ships may become absolutely necessary, sooner than we realize, because among major raw materials, the United States is now *self-sufficient only in coal, molyb-*

denum, phosphate, and *magnesium!* Wood and petroleum (fuel oil) have shifted from net exports to net imports, and we are variously deficient in asbestos, tin, manganese, iron ore, bauxite, cobalt, nickel, chromite, quartz crystal, and industrial diamonds. Although some of these products can be shipped by air, they would still be at the mercy of the same elements—weather at sea. While visible shipping exports from the United States still greatly exceed imports, our imports of essential raw materials and food products are rising steadily; a continuing increase in exports at the best economic levels is necessary for the future stability and dynamic growth of America.

Ship design is also important, calling for more technical or marine engineering. Today freight costs for ocean cargoes vary quite widely with the type of cargo and the distance and route carried. The Maritime Administration has recently advanced the idea of designing ships specifically for certain limited trade routes. Thus construction costs could be reduced by building certain ships for use on voyages that *do not have to withstand continuously rough seas,* such as those in polar regions. Recognizing also the value of speed of delivery for certain light cargoes, varying freight rates might assist express ships, similar to the rail express and air freight systems.

Tragic Loss of U.S.S. "Thresher"

The tragic loss of the submarine U.S.S. *Thresher* reveals the urgency of two unusual requirements based on oceanography and ocean engineering. First, we must know more about the sea areas in which we routinely conduct special tests, such as deep dives. For example, at the time of the *Thresher* disaster, a violent late-winter storm may have changed drastically the normal current regime near the mouth of the Gulf of Maine. This change, together with internal waves, may have disturbed the horizontal distribution of water density enough to have affected or upset the *Thresher's* ability to maintain depth control.

Second, we need to learn how to do many things on the bottom of the ocean in *a controlled and systematic way.* These include the investigation of accidents, recovery of lost hardware, adjustment or maintenance of bottom equipment, and detailed bottom surveys for various purposes, both civilian and military.

The recent report of the Navy's Deep Submergence Systems Review Group brought many of these problems into focus. Efforts to improve deep-water engineering capability will depend in part, it found, on detailed oceanographic knowledge—currents, internal waves, sea-floor topography, bottom sediment and rock characteristics, biology, acoustical properties, and behavior of visible light in the deep sea. From them may depend the safety of the nation if a Communist attack is spearheaded by submarines, as some experts believe it might be. All of which warrants that *more than the tiny one per cent* of the Navy's total budget might well be spent for oceanographic research, for even the use and safeguarding of the Navy itself.

Comparison with U.S.S.R.

How does Russia's oceanography in general compare with ours today? While the Soviet Union has larger ships (a few of them) than any vessels the Free World has in current use, the difference in size is the result of special needs rather than a reflection on the United States' ability to construct bigger vessels. Russian ships must travel farther at sea to attain the most desirable world areas for research, fishing, or many varieties of oceanographic work. Consequently, Soviet vessels must carry more food, personnel, and equipment than ships of nations which are easily accessible to the better oceanographic seas.

Recently (1964) a group of six American scientists were invited to make a conducted tour of oceanographic installations in the Soviet Union. No doubt the trip was planned to give the best effect on the visitors, but a surprising amount of information not too favorable for the Soviets was divulged.

The consensus of the six U.S. oceanographers who made the trip was that the Soviet Union may lead both Japan and the United Kingdom in its total efforts to explore the ocean, but it is behind the United States and in some respects it is apparently not catching up. There are, however, certain areas where the six scientists admit that the Russians know no peers. The most significant of these is in Arctic Ocean studies, where, not only does the effort exceed that of the United

States, but their methods are described as both thorough and good. The Russians are also thought to excel in turbulence studies.

Yet No Mini-Subs

As for the number of "well qualified" oceanographers in Russia, the group is estimated at about 1,000; and of shipping devoted specifically to oceanographic research, the total may be 50,000 gross tons. Aside from one converted World War II submarine, the *R/V Severyanka*, used primarily for fisheries research (watching undersea fish schools, nets, and trawls) the Russians have no deep-diving, free-swimming research craft. One such, similar to Woods Hole's new *Alvin*, and to be called *Sever II* (*North II*), is now in the design stage. The Russians do have four tethered diving chambers (called bathystats); these are winched over the side of a ship and have a depth capability of about 1,800 feet.

The Soviet Navy appears to play considerably less of a role in Russian oceanography than the U.S. Navy does in this country's efforts. In both Soviet laboratories and aboard research ships, the ratio of women to men is high—at all levels of technical competence, from technician through academician. The U.S. travelers got the impression that most Russian oceanographers have acquired an engineering degree somewhere along the way—although they are now primarily listed as scientists.

In *Navy*, the magazine for the Navy League, December 1964, Captain T. K. Treadwell, Jr., who accompanied the U.S.S.R. tour as Assistant Oceanographer of the Navy for Plans and Policies, reports:

> "In addition to Moscow State University, the focal point of education in USSR oceanography, the Universities of Leningrad and Vladivostok also have chairs in oceanography; the Institute of Marine Engineering and Hydrometeorological Institute of Leningrad also train oceanographers. About 60 are graduated annually at the lower lever and 5 at the doctoral level. In spite of all this it is still necessary to draft oceanographers from other disciplines, especially in physics, chemistry and mathematics."

Spread Across Many Agencies

Speaking of the U.S.S.R.'s overall oceanography, Captain Treadwell continues:

"As in the United States, it is spread across many agencies, following different courses. Although the Soviets have two major coordinating committees (similar to our own Interagency Committee on Oceanography), it does not appear that their coordinating is any more effective than ours, and more likely less. On the other hand, much firmer direction can be exercised in the USSR if and when it is considered necessary. . . . The actual numbers of oceanographic ships are almost impossible to compare. The Soviets have a far larger ship-of-opportunity program in operation and these are hard to identify and evaluate. . . . The shore facilities of the Soviet oceanographic institutions are surely the worst part of their program. Research centers are domiciled in rundown country palaces of the last century, or stuck in basements of apartment houses. Crowding was the rule; lighting, heating and general office support equipment were ancient.

"In summary, the Soviet oceanographic program is massive and slanted toward practical application (such as ice prediction, fisheries, engineering work and coastal control). It is being carried out by large numbers of average people, led by top-flight scientists, under the disadvantage of commonplace equipment and poor working conditions. Significances have been made in the last twenty years and the trend will doubtless continue. . . . At the moment, it would seem that Russia is getting as much for their money as we are, in the form of practical applications. They seem to lack a strong program of fundamental research, which is clearly necessary to provide the basis of achievements a decade or generations in the future."

As a kind of footnote, Captain Treadwell observes:

"It would be equally shortsighted of the United States to neglect those phases of its own effort which are lagging, such as education, shipbuilding and development of practical applications. This visit provided the opportunity to see a part of the Soviet program. Perhaps even more important than that is the opportunity to see the United

States program in a new context, so that we can correct our weaknesses and take advantage of our strengths."

Special Legislation Needed

To return to our domestic oceanic problems and how they are related to the outside world: The high seas belong to no man and to no nation, yet they have always and probably will be used forever by many men and many nations. For certain modern needs, however, international understanding and agreement must be found. To mention a simple instance, fishes of the high seas are widely and unevenly distributed; some marine creatures wander over great distances, and their distribution and abundance changes in the oceanic environment, sometimes to the point of extinction. International cooperation among marine biologists, obtained through national groups (such as Congress) is needed on a systematic basis.

The task of making detailed maps of the ocean floor requires the continuous operation, over several decades, of many well-equipped vessels and an international navigation network. If this great task can be shared among all interested nations, the expenses to any one or two countries would not be as burdensome or tardy as they are today. Oceanographers throughout the world require much more information about important activities that occur only in limited areas. Examples are coral atolls, deep-sea trenches, volcanic island chains (and new volcanic islands, such as Surtsey, off Iceland); boundary currents on the western side of oceans, such as the Gulf Stream and the Black Current or Kuroshio, and the monsoon reversals of winds and currents in the Indian Ocean and the South China Sea.

Ideas Plus Hardware

The simplest form of international cooperation is the exchange of ideas and techniques between individual scientists of different countries, through visits to laboratories, cruises on ships of various countries, and international scientific meetings. But much more is required. A nation must also help to supply ships, instrumentation, fuel and food, and the personnel that operate vessels at sea. Such activities must be balanced against the actual costs, not only in money but also in the diversion of scarce scientific personnel from research and from other work on smaller-scale problems of interest, primarily to individuals or individual countries. The mechanism of international cooperation, as it now stands, is always clumsy and demands a great deal of unexpected time and devotion from many people.

However, there can be no denying that a well-run, well-painted oceanographic ship in a foreign port, dedicated to advancing knowledge, is one of the best means of increasing respect for the nation involved, and in gaining strength in the unity of science. Our cooperation with the Japanese, for instance, has given both nations a greater understanding of the social and economic factors that affect the thoughts and actions of American and Japanese scientists, to our common advantage.

More Joining of Hands

Because almost all studies of the ocean are expensive and require many men, ships, and special equipment in three areas (over, on, and under the sea), the nations of the world are being forced, for economic reasons, to join hands in more cooperative ventures, as they did during the very creditable International Geophysical Year, and as they continue to do so peacefully in Antarctica. Largest and latest of these special enterprises is the International Indian Ocean Expedition (1962–1965), in which the United States government is making available several ships and some personnel to be operated by oceanographic institutions. More than a score of nations, including the U.S.S.R., are participating in this pioneering expedition with ships and men.

Another special enterprise is the International Cooperative Investigations of the Tropical Atlantic, an attempt to obtain, in a certain limited area and time, a series of oceanic measurements—actually the first large-scale synoptic survey. Still another is the International Year of the Quiet Sun, which involves considerable oceanographic interest, particularly in studies of meteorology. Phase II of the Mohole Project will no doubt finally take place in international waters because the closest place to obtain a sample of the earth's mantle is from a sea platform. Drilling tests are also taking place on land in southwest Texas.

One of the most promising oceanic international meetings

was held in March 1964, in Tokyo. Under the auspices of the United States–Japan Cooperative Science Program, seven Japanese and seven American scientists planned an extensive program on physical oceanography of the Pacific Ocean. The meeting called for a series of recording stations along the Asiatic and North Pacific coasts and at island stations in the Pacific Ocean which would supply a continuous flow of data on observations of temperature, salinity, sea level, standard meterological elements, and solar radiation.

Buoys Need Radio Frequencies

Felix Favorite, of the Bureau of Commercial Fisheries Laboratory, Seattle, has put forth a proposal based on his group's experiments with drifting, interrogating-transponding telemetry buoys. It is his aim to obtain continuous oceanographic and meteorological observations in the open ocean by use of *drifting*, rather than *anchored*, buoys. However, another school of thought wants the buoys lashed to certain moorings. This is the so-called "Moore buoy," designed for the Office of Naval Research by the Convair Division of General Dynamics. In its initial tests in September 1964, this 50,000-pound "floating saucer," 40 feet in diameter and 7 feet thick, was moored in 300 feet of water about 5 miles off the coast of Miami in the Strait of Florida (Gulf Stream). The place was selected in hope that this unmanned First Ocean Data Station, to call it by its proper name, would be exposed to a full-scale hurricane that would serve to verify its seaworthiness. It was, and it did.

This victory is but part of the battle which must be won before either drifting or fixed buoys can be placed throughout the world. One of the unsolved problems is getting enough radio frequencies assigned to such buoys so that they may report their complete information to shore stations. Two world bodies are thrashing this out. The trouble is that all the high-frequency channels were allocated on an international basis at Geneva in 1960, and oceanographers' needs may not have been fully apparent then.

Now, however, a committee of oceanographers, headed by Dr. James M. Snodgrass, of La Jolla, California, is trying to worm some frequencies away from other allocations in negotiations. Because the effort includes some 40 nations, it will take time. Meanwhile, Snodgrass said, some bilateral agreements have been worked up for interim testing. He estimates that five years will be needed before a significant number of the buoys can be constructed and equipped. This may give the World Meteorological Organization and the Intergovernment Oceanographic Commission time to line up some worldwide frequencies.

Upper Mantle Project

Let us return a moment to the International Upper Mantle Project, whose aim is to study intensively the outermost 600 miles of the earth's surface, by land and by sea. While some work, that would have been done anyway by the U.S. Geological Survey and U.S. Coast and Geodetic Survey, has been contributed to the program, the U.S. share is presently inadequate. Meanwhile the Russians are going well ahead, doing Upper Mantle work and producing papers, and the Canadians have completed their share and produced a final report.

Likewise, the International Year of the Quiet Sun—U.S. participation, at least—is getting under way slowly. An excellent booklet describing this two-year (1964-1965) effort was published in December 1964 by the National Science Foundation. With graphs, sketches, and photographs it explains how scientists of more than 60 nations are joined in an effort of geophysical observations and measurements of the sun, timed to coincide with the occurrence of *minimum* solar activity during 1964 and 1965. The project thus complements the International Geophysical Year, 1957–1958, held so successively during a period of *maximum* solar activity.

Saving the Whaling Industry

For many years, one of the most commendable groups for cooperative efforts in the sea, the International Whaling Commission, did much to save the whaling industry from extinction. Now both the Commission and the whales seem to be threatened, possibly doomed. The four nations which sent whaling fleets to the Antarctic (the Netherlands, Norway, the Soviet Union, and Japan) have rejected the scientific advice of the IWC concerning the limits of the 1964–1965 season's catch. Consequently, the finback whale may be hunted out of existence.

An official statement, issued after the meeting of the Commission, mentions the blue whale, whose numbers were considered so limited that extinction was thought possible. All the delegates agreed, however, to almost total protection of this species, the world's largest living creature. The entire whaling problem has now been referred to the International Union for Conservation of Nature and Natural Resources, based in Switzerland, and there are hopes that the question will be raised in the United Nations General Assembly by the Food and Agriculture Organization. If this fails, some whales may still exist when enough of the animals have been taken to make whaling nonprofitable, thus permitting eventual replenishment of the schools.

New Sources for Fresh Water?

Unless nations find new techniques to improve management and control of their fresh water resources, critical shortages will result soon in many parts of the world. It is estimated that the world population will double and consumption of water will triple by the end of the century.

While much effort, in the United States, is going into desalinization—the removal of salts from the ocean water or from brackish inland supplies—hydrologists believe other sources will have to be obtained, including natural underground reservoirs and artificial wells and the raising of water tables. As the problem is worldwide, a long-range program, called the International Hydrological Decade, began on January 1, 1965. Each country is responsible for its own program but overall planning will be coordinated through the United Nations Educational, Scientific and Cultural Organization and other international organizations—because rivers, watersheds, weather, and other related water phenomena do not respect national boundaries.

Most Lie in Dusty Pigeonholes

Sooner or later Congress will have to come to grips with the burgeoning interest in oceanography evidenced by government agencies, various industries, foundations, universities, and the public in general. No fewer than 40 Congressional committees and subcommittees have been involved in appropriating or authorizing funds to be spent on oceano-

206 • NEW WORLDS OF OCEANOGRAPHY

graphic programs; and several bills dealing with oceanography are to be submitted shortly to Congress.

It is not the function of this book to beat the drums for any particular piece of proposed legislation (although the author has his own definite preferences and opinions about them); but it is to be hoped that the readers of this book will inform themselves on the issues and make their own opinions known to their Congressmen.

At the very least, the importance and urgency of action in oceanography are unmistakable, and have been recognized in the 1964 platforms of the Democratic and Republican Parties. For example, here is a section of the Democratic platform:

> Provide the people of this nation a balanced outdoor recreation program to add to their health and well-being, including the addition of improved management of national parks, forests, lakeshores, seashores and recreation areas. . . . Increase our stock of wildlife and fish. . . . Continue and strengthen the dynamic program inaugurated to assure fair treatment for American fishermen and the preservation of fishing rights . . . . Continue the attack we have launched on the polluted air that envelopes our cities and on eliminating the pollution of our rivers and streams. . . . Continue to promote the development of new and improved methods of generating electric power, such as the recent gains in the field of atomic energy and the Passamaquoddy tidal power. . . . Unlock the resources of the sea through a strong oceanography program. . . . Intensify our efforts to solve the critical water problems of many sections of this country by desalinization. . . .

"Crash Research Program"

As for the President himself, Mr. Johnson has not yet pinpointed his attention directly on the marine sciences—with one exception. On November 20, 1964, after an all-day meeting with the Secretary of the Interior, Stewart L. Udall, Mr. Johnson ordered a "crash research program" to convert more saline water to fresh water. The President plans to ask the 89th Congress for an additional $16 million for this program. The object: to cut the price of desalted fresh water from $1 a thousand gallons to 25¢ or 35¢—a little more than the cost of "branch water" delivered to an ordinary city tap.

Presidential interest in saline water, converted from brackish wells and the sea, gives encouragement to the oceanic community that Mr. Johnson may again take a direct personal hand in advancing other marine interests. In his State-of-the-Union message, in addition to another strong appeal "to bring closer the day when the oceans will supply our growing need for fresh water," there were mentions of more seashore parks to protect our heritage, and "legal power to prevent pollution of our air and water before it happens. . . . We will increase research to learn more about control of pollution."

Kennedy's Sea Goals

Meanwhile, President Johnson may draw upon another worthy precept from the late President John F. Kennedy, given shortly before his death, on the occasion of the 100th Anniversary of the National Academy of Sciences:

> "Our goal is to investigate the world ocean, its boundaries, its properties, its processes. To a surprising extent, the sea has remained a mystery. Ten thousand fleets still sweep over it in vain. We know less of the oceans at our feet, where we came from, than we do of the sky above our heads. It is time to change this, to use to the full our powerful new instruments of oceanic exploration, to drive back the frontiers of the unknown in the waters which encircle our globe. I can imagine no [more important] field among all those which are so exciting today than this great effort which our country and others will carry on in years to come."

INDEX

Abyssal plains, and other depths; 91

Agassiz, Jones and Alexander; father and son; oceanic research and instruments; 42

Alexander the Great, as early diver; 36

Allan Hancock Research Foundation; 133, 134

Aluminaut, larger deep-sea all-aluminum non-military submersible; 48

Alvin, medium-sized sub designed for oceanic research; funded by office of Naval Research; 48

AMSOC, disbanded group, (American Miscellaneous Society); 97, 102

Antarctica, ice cap and sea level; 30
    Cooperation among nations in science there, etc.; 202

Anti-submarine warfare (ASW), p.; 182
    Increase of USN appropriations for; 183
    Sound navigation ranging (SONAR); 184
    Need more about ocean depths by research; 184
    To "see" yet be "unseen"; 186

Aquariums general, see Laboratories, seaside; 44

"Aquotels", proposed resorts under sea; 196

Archealogy, underwater studies of; 50, 51

Argonaut, octopod that lives in rare nautilus shell; 87

Atolls, coral islands; 91, 111, 201

ASWEPS, Antisubmarine Warfare Environmental Prediction System; 174

ATMOS, use of atmosphere in warfare study; 148
    synoptic weather research; 149

AUTEC, Atlantic Underwater Test and evaluation center; Bahamas; 174

Bahamas, Bimini; 86, 87

Bascom, Willard, marine engineer; 98, 99

Bathymetry, bottom topography methods; 177
    —Echo sounder or an oscillograph, use of; 177
    —Microcontouring, camera process; 189

210 • NEW WORLDS OF OCEANOGRAPHY

Bathythermograph (or "B.T."), records water temperatures as function of depth while towed by a vessel underway; 171, 178
—Electronic bathythermograph; 173
—Still produced in quantities; 180
Baylor, Dr. E. R. of Woods Hale Oceanographic Institution; 83
Beebe, William, bathysphere; 18, 33, 45
Berman, Alan, of Columbia University's Hudson Laboratories; 67
Barnard, J. Laurens, of Allan Hancock Foundation; 134
Bioluminescence ("Phosphorescence" to landlubbers); 76
Brown, Dr. Harrison; 193
Bottom-bounce, effect on ASW operations; 191
Buoy, stable oceanographic platform; 175
—Moored, to accomodate more data; 181
—"Moore buoy" unmanned First ocean data Station; 203

Celsius, formerly known as Centigrade temperature; 180
Canada, completes its share of upper Mantle Project; 204
Cetacean Research (Whales and Porpoises); 81
"Chain of the sea", plants and animal life; 74
Challenger, HM.S; first major oceanographic cruise, 1872-76; unusual scientific cargo; 43, 55
Chemistry frontier of sea; 124
Coast and Geoditic Survey, sea level trends from tide gauges; 31
—First Federal scientific organization; 41
—Tidal Current Tables; 63
—R.V. Pioneer off Ceylon; 109
—Stereo cameras in ocean floor mapping; 189
Coast Guard, as a military service; 192
—Congress gives greater authority in oceanography; 192
Coast Survey, first Federal scientific organization in USA; later became Coast & Geodetic Survey; 41
Coates, Rear Adm. L. D., U.SN; 180
Continental drift, theory of; 25
Coastline, USA, second longest; 16
Coelacanth, "living fossil"; 21, 22
Columbus, Christopher, early sea research; 37, 38
Congeries, a combination of several sciences; 34
Congress, attempts to obtain appropriations for more ocean-

ographic programs; 205
—Bills presented; 206; 207
Cooperation, need for among maritime nations; 202
Cores, found during "Mohole" drilling; 100
Cores, oceanic, types of instruments; 176
—Phlager, Erving and Kullenberg cores; 177
Corialis force, deflects sea water currents because of earth's rotation; 65
Cosmos Club, Washington, D.C.; 97
Crab, horseshoe; world's oldest surviving inhabitant; 20
Craft, (ships, subs, and planes) need and uses for on sea; 35
Cromwell, Townsend; discovered deep sea undercurrents of Pacific 1952, while studying tuna fishing methods; 63
Currents, submerged or counter, such as Cromwell in Pacific depths; 56
Currents, surface: Gulf Stream, El Nino Humboldt, Japan's Kuroshio, etc.; 56, 58, 59
Currents, tidal; horizontal flow as current floods and ebbs; 60
Currents, types of, reversing, rotary, velocity, etc.; 62
"Cuss I", barge used in Mohole, Phase I; 98

Darwin, Charles; "Origin of the Species"; 42
Deep Submergence Systems Review Group; 186
—Navy's Recent report of; 198
Deepest depth in sea; echo-sounding; by man; 108
Depot of Charts and Instruments, Navy; origin of; 39
Diamonds from sea, S.W. Africa; 122
Douglas, Marjory Stoneman; writer; 140
Dredges for sea bottom samplers; 177
—Types of: orange peel, clam shell snapper, bottom; 177
Drift bottles, purpose of; 68, 178
Drifter, for bottom current studies; 70

Eaton, William, first depth sea marker; 39
Eckman current meter, to determine timed interval; 179
Eltanin, USNS, floating research laboratory of National Science Foundation; 55
Engineering, oceanic; 163, 196
—Marine, need for new ship design; 197
Estaurine, or tidewater fresh and salt water areas; 161

Evolution, "community theory of; 83
Ewing, Dr. John L, see Dr. Maurice Ewing, brother; 27
Ewing, Dr. Maurice, director of Columbia University's Lamont Geological Observatory; 27, 29
—Original group to set up "Mohole"; 97
Explorers, part in oceanography; 34

"False bottom," due to ooze layers absorbing sound; 190
Fetch—the distance the waves have run under the drive of the sea; 71
Fish and Fisheries, U.S. Commission of; first Federal conservation agency; 42 Need for accurate census of sea animals today; 158
Fisheries, world catch, USA now fifth below Japan, Peru, Communist China and Soviet Russia; 162
Fishing—still a hunting process; 150
  use of bait and nets; 150
  New electronic fishing equipment; 150
  The fishery scientist; 152
  Farming the sea; 152
  Purse seins; 153
  Otter trawls; 153
Fisheries, Bureau of Commercial; 88
  own oceanic ships and land laboratories; 159
  Federal point of view, "operation Trident"; 160
  Research operations and expeditions; 160
  Electrotrawling; 161
  Studying medium-sized submarine; 161
Fishery Industry, legislation needed; 167
  —Conflicts international; 168
  —Territorial limits; 168
FLIP, floating and tilted instrument platform, manned; 51
"Flying the flag", benefits derived from USA oceanic prestige in foreign ports; 195
Forrestal, James, first secretary of Defense; 18
Franklin, Benjamin, first chart of Gulf Stream; 38
Frequencies, radio bands needed for operation of unmanned buoys; 203

Galler, Dr. S. R., of office of Naval Research; 81
Galtsoff, Dr. Paul S., shellfish expert; 89
Geology, Marine
  —Deep cores and samples; 176

INDEX • 213

—"Texas Towers"; 91, 123
—Dredging for minerals, including diamonds; 122
—"Mohole"; 91
Gravimeter, geophysical measure of gravity; 177
 Also see Vening Meinesz pendulum; 177
Groves, Don., National Academy of Sciences; 179
Gulf Stream, characteristics; operation Gulf Stream; 62
 fastest sea current; 38, 57, 58, 59, 62
Guantanamo, US Naval base, saline water; 118
Guyot, flat-topped undersea mountain, far from continents and Islands; 91, 110

Henry, Joseph; first secretary of the Smithsonian; 42
Henry the Navigator, Portuguese, early mariner and sea explorer; 37
"High Seas," see Treaty of Seas; 119
Hull, Seabrook, "The Bountiful Sea"; 132
Hurricanes, early studies; 38
"Hurricane Hunters," plane patrols of storms; 139
 —Weather satellites; 145, 148
Hurricanes, names for ("Dana", "Hazel" or "Cleo".); 138
 —"Advisories"; 138
 —Radiosonde via balloons; 139
 —What "triggers" them; 141
 —Seeding with silver iodide; 142
Hydrological Decade, International, began Jan. 1, 1965; 205
 —Plans to tap underground reservoirs and raise water tables; 205
Hydrometer, measures density of sea water; 176
 Copenhagen standard sea water sample; 177
Hydrophone, a form of undersea microphone; 177
Hydrophotometer, water clarity device; 178
Hess, Harry H. of Princeton, N.J., geologist; 97

Indian Ocean Expedition, International (IIOE) p.; 52, 93
Instrumentation, needed aboard ship
 —Gadgets fashioned at sea; 169
 —New devices; 170, 179
 —To obtain sea samples, depth, and latitude and longitude, via shoran, lorac, and loran; 179
 —Future needs of; 179-80
 —Oceanographic Instrumentation Center; 182

Interagency Committee on Oceanography; 192
International Cooperative Investigation of the Tropical Atlantic (ICITA), synoptic survey; 54, 93
International Oceanographic Foundation, "Sea Frontiers"; 125
"Interstitial," water squeezed from space between deep-sea cores; 124
Isotopes, plus side of radio-active materials; 129

Japanese, Cooperation in oceanography; 203
—Currents, Black or Kuroshio; 201
—Light from sea animals; 76-7
Johnson, President L. B., statements re oceanography and marine sciences; 206-7

Kennedy, President John F.; 10
—100th Anniversary of National Academy Sciences, sea goals; 207

Laboratory, seaside; developments scientific and entertainment (Aquarium); 44
Latimeria chalumnar, coelacanth or "living fossil"; 22, 23
Laws of the Sea, need for uniformity among
—State fisheries; 158
—Last sail-work fleet; 157
Lerner Laboratory, Bimini, Bahamas, T-V underseas; 86
Lilites, marine animal; 24
Limulus polyphemus (horseshoe crab); 20
Link, Edwin A.; *spid*; underwater archeology; 50
LOCO, Long cores of U. of Miami geology program; 105
Long, E. John; career, publications; 18
Lorac, long range accuracy at sea; 179
Loran, long range navigation system; 179

MacDonald, Dr. Gordon J. F., geophysicist, Univ. of California, Los Angeles, Cal.; 32, 33
McHugh, Dr. J. L., assistant director for Biological Research, Bureau of Commercial Fisheries; 152
—Long-line tuna fishery; 152
MAD, magnetic anomaly detector; 190
Magnetism, evidence of continental drift; 26
Magnuson, Senator Warren G.; 12
—Oceanography bills in Senate; 206

INDEX • 215

Mantle, largest and least known constituent of the earth, rock; 91

Maps, as strategic weapons; 37
—Continuous operations shared in international navigation network; 201

Marine Science, Institute of (Univ. of Miami); 86, 87, 110
—Tagging program for pelagic fish; 165

"Marine Snow"; 83, 84

Marlin, large pelagic fish; 87

MARS, Mobile Atlantic Range System, beacons on ocean floor; 175

Maury, Matthew Fontaine; first systomatic study of oceans; 39, 40

Maxwell, Arthur E., office of Naval Research; 97

Menhaden, greatest catch by weight of North American fisheries; 153

Mesocaph, mid-depth submarine; named for *Auguste Piccard*, famed Swiss scientist, by his son, Dr. Jacques Piccard; 47

Meteor, German ship, attempted to obtain gold from sea; 120

Meteorites, bombardment of earth by; 19

Meteorology, weather at sea; 178
—Instruments used: Anemometer, hygrometer, sling psychrometer, barometer, recording pyrheliometer; 178

Miami, University of, see Marine Science

Mineral, most precious in world (fresh water); 111
—other minerals in sea; 120
—compounds of salt; 121
—"maritime" mining; 125

"Mineral Mines", solid metals from sea; nodules; 121

Mini-subs, small non military undersea research vessels; 46
—Soviet Union lacks; 199

Missiles, submarines; 15

Mohole, geological-marine project; 30, 94-105
—Phase II, plans for; 202

Mohorovicic, Andrya, Yugoslav seismologist; 95

Monsoons, reversals of winds and currents in Indian Ocean; 201

Munk, Walter, of Scripps; one of originators of "Mohole" Phase I; 97

Nansen, Fredtjof, Norwegian explorer; 170

216 • NEW WORLDS OF OCEANOGRAPHY

—Nansen bottle, samples water at different depths; 170, 176
—Quantities still produced; 180
NASCO, National Academy Sciences Committee on Oceanography; 195, 196
National Academy of Science, charter and mission; 42
—"Economic Benefits from Oceanographic Research 1964."; 195
—100th Anniversary, speech by President Kennedy, re sea goals; 207
National Geographic Society, Gulf Stream explorations; 59
National Oceanographic Data Center; 181
National Science Foundation, oceanic work; 55
Nautiloids, ancestors of modern nautilus shell; 25
Nautilus, rare seashell; 87
Naval Research Reviews, publication of office of Naval Research; 181
Navigation, on, under and over the sea; 170
—Satellite navigation; 170-1
Navy, magazine of the Navy League; 199
Navy Yard Annex, Washington DC.; 92, 172, 182
Nodules, see "Mineral Mines"

Ocean Science News, newsletter, Washington DC; 160
Oceanographers, training of; 17
Oceanography, definition of; 7
Oceanography, long range goals; 9
Oceanography, research and survey ships; 14
Oceanology, obsolete term for oceanography; 45
Oceanographic Instrumentation Center, Navy Yard Annex, Washington DC; 172
Oceanographic Sorting Center, Smithsonian; 54
Oil, drilling from sea; 123
"Otter boards" or trawls, see Fishing; 153
Oxford, Md., oyster research laboratory of Bureau of Commercial Fisheries; 89
Oysters, early history as food, p.; 88
—Present day diseases, p.; 88, 89

Paleomagnetism, new science reviving old theory of continents joined; 25
Peru's new fisheries, anchovetta; 162
Pelagic, large, open sea fish; 164

INDEX • 217

Piccard, Auguste, name for mesocaph of Dr. Jacques Piccards father; mid-depth submarine; 47
Plankton, drifting, teeming tiny life of the sea described; 74
—Half meter plankton net; 176
—Clarke Bumpus sampler for; 176
—Hardy recorder for; 176
Polaris, firing nuclear submarine missile; 184
—First sea test, 1960; 186
Political platforms, re oceanography; 206
Pollution of Sea, radioactive wastes; 126
—fallout from nuclear weapon tests; 127
—poisoning from plankton chain reaction; 128
Porpoise, sonar-like navigating device; 78
Portuguese man-of-war; 83
Portulans, or Portolanos, special books for early navigators, with charts; 37
Protein, edible from fish flour; 166
Purse sein, fishery tuna catches; 152

Quiet Sun, International year of; 204

Why "R's" in certain oyster months?; 158
Raborn, Admiral William F.,
—Weather in warfare; 148
—Fog dissipation in warfare; 148
Radar, underwater, attempts to use; 190
Radioisotopes, "half-lives"; 129
—use in medical and agricultural research, "tracers"; 130
—power generators; 130
—undersea navigation beacon; 131
—food preservation; 131
"Railroad Worm"; 77
Revelle, Dr. Roger; 117
Ridge, mid-Atlantic and other sea mountains, mostly submerged; 109
Riley, Dr. Gordon, of Yale U.; 83
"Rivers of Mud", current in sea; 68
Runcorn, S. K., University of Durham, England; 26, 27

Saline Water, office of (Dept. of the Interior); 113, 114, 115
—other water sources needed; 205

—"crash research program" requested by President Johnson; 206
Salinometer, salt content instrument; 175
"Scattering Layers" sound reflecting zones; 82
   —Report by Vincent J. Marteka in *Sea Frontiers*, May 1964; 82, 83
Science, birth pains in USA; 41
   Aims of Federal government; 93
Scripps Institution on Oceanography; 30, 44
   First informal meeting of AMSOC group re "Mohole"; 97
Sealab, deep sea capsule for manned research in depths; 49
Sea, as origin of all life; 20, 84, 85
Sea levels, "apparent" rise of; 32
   —Rising and sinking periods; 32
Sea sounds, biological (sonar); 85, 86
Seas, freedom of the (political); 15
Seawater, not drinkable, but many uses; 35
Secchi disc, early device to measure water depths; 178
Seiches, sea waves from barometric pressure; 106
Seismic Sea Wave Warning System, Pacific; network of 60 tide stations; 41
"Seven"—why it is a mystic word at sea; 70
Shark, ancestry of; 23
Sharks, a "Dinner bell" for; 79
Sharks, repelling devices for men and nets; 81
   —Shark Search Panel; 81
Shepard, Dr. Francis, oceanographer, Scripps Institution of Oceanography; 30
Shimomura, Dr. Osamu, of Nagoya Univ. of Japan; 76
Siphonophores, transparent sea creatures whose bladders reflect sound; 83
Shoran, short range navigation; 179
Smith, Dr. F. G. Walton, editor "Sea Frontier" and president of International Oceanographic Foundation, Miami; 36, 37
Smith, Professor J. L. B., South African ichthyologist; 22
"Sniffers," means of detecting schools of fish; 164
Snodgrass, Dr. James J.; 203
SONAR, sound navigation ranging; 184
SOOP, Submarine oceanographic Observation Program; 174

Soviet Russia,
- —Use of underwater fisheries research; 162
- —Soviet submarine used for research on commercial fisheries; 162
- —Whaling in Antarctic; 166

Soviet Russia, military forces, submarines
- —Potential opponent U.S.A.; 182
- —Uses of Soviet offensive operations; 183
- —Soviet range of missiles; 185
- —Comparison Soviet oceanography with USA; 198-200
- —Lack of mini-subs; 199
- —Women ratio to men high; 199

Soviet Russia, marine fishing vessels; 14, 198

Space, outer, versus oceans; 13

SPAR, Seagoing Platform for Acoustic Research, unmanned; 51

Spid, inflated rubber tent designed by inventor Edwin A. Link; 50

"Station", halt at sea where scientific observations are recorded; 43
- —Samples obtained; 176

Stewart, Dr. Harris B. Jr., chief oceanographer, US Coast and Geodetic Survey; 54, 66

Storms, major ones at sea:
  hurricanes, typhoons, "baguios" (Philippines), "reppus" (Japan), "willy willies" (Australia) and "asifa-a" (Arabia); 136

Submarines military capabilities of; 185
- —Need of marine science, pro and con; 185
- —Deep diving test areas; 197

SUBROC, submarine-launched "flying torpedo"; 187

Supple, John J., Maryland Tuna Corporation; 164

Surtsey, newest volcano island, off Iceland; 108
- —More information for such limited areas needed; 201

Sutcliffe, Dr. W. H., Lehigh U.; 83

Taylor, F. B., American scientist; 26

Television, marine study of; 86, 122

Temperature, variations at sea, significance of; 73

"Texas Towers," sea rigs; 91, 123

Thermocline, water depth levels where temperature changes quickly from warm to cool; 134
- —Sonar ranges reworked for; 191

Thermometer, airborne Radiation of; 173
—Deep Sea reversing Thermometer; 176
Thresher, USS, submarine lost at sea 1963; 186
—Areas for such tests, deep dives; 197
Thresher, U.S. submarine, sunk off Cape Cod in April 1963; 47
Tide, sea forces from sun and moon that rise and fall vertically; 60
"Tidal Waves", misnomer, (see Tsunami); 68
"Tilt," beware earth's axis of; 33
—Also on "Cuss I" of "Mohole"; 99
Treasure hunting, undersea recreation; 196
Treaty of sea, need for international compact; 119
Treadwell, Capt. T. K. Jr., USN; 199, 200
Tribolites, extinct marine fossil; 20, 24
Trieste (I and II), bathyscopes of Swiss Piccards; 47
Tsunami, Japanese term for seismic sea waves; 68
—1964 Aleutian earthquake & tsunami, p.; 107
Tuna, New England tests for fishing and canning; 165

Upper Mantle Project, International; 204

Velocimeters, sound of; 172, 178

Wallen, Dr. I. E., Smithsonian oceanographer; 54, 135
Wangersky, Dr. P. J., of Yale U.; 84
Warfare, Submarine and anti submarine; 82
—mapping of sea bottom; 93
Wastes—detergents, insecticides, sewage bilge oil, defoliants, human and industrial wastes; 132
Water, fresh; shortages today; 112
—reclaiming sewage water; 113
Water, fresh; growing needs; 112
Water, saline water methods; descaling; 113, 119
Waves, terms of, described by oceanographers and navigators; 66, 67
Wave heights, shipboard recorder; 173
Wegener, Dr. Alfred, German meteorologist; 25
Whales, subsonic sounds; 78, 81
Whaling, industry on verge of collapse; 166
—International Whaling Commission; 166
—Three principal whaling fleets; 166

—Finback whale doomed?; 204
—Final survival of whales; 205
Whittington, Dr. H. B., Harvard geologist; 24
Wisby, Dr. Warren J., Univ. of Miami; 79
Woods Hole, Mass; origin as oceanic center; "The Fisheries"; 44
Woods Hole Oceanographic Institution,
—Investigation of western Atlantic tuna; 165
—Thermistors aboard *R.V. Chain*; 171
—Stable Oceanographic buoy; 175
—*R. V. Alvin*, research mini-sub; 199

**Electrifying
Brilliant
Delightful**

LOUIS NIZER

MY LIFE IN COURT N-836/95¢
This headline-studded casebook recreates some of the most suspenseful and talked-about courtroom dramas of modern times.

THINKING ON YOUR FEET X-880/60¢
A wise and witty look at the art of holding an audience—a treasury of quips, quotes, and sharply-etched characterizations of the great and near great.

BETWEEN YOU AND ME X-965/60¢
Brilliant observations of the great and famous men of our time—essays on topics that affect all our lives—wry comments on things that amuse or irritate everyone.

> **NOTE:** Add 10¢ postage and handling charges for every book ordered. Pyramid pays postage on orders for four books or more.

------WHEREVER PAPERBACKS ARE SOLD OR USE THIS COUPON--

PYRAMID BOOKS
Dept. K-131, 444 Madison Avenue, New York, N.Y. 10022

Please send me the LOUIS NIZER books circled below. I enclose
$_____

N-836   X-880   X-965

Name_____

Street Address_____

City_____ State_____ Zip_____

Which Of These Have You Missed?

BESTSELLING NON-FICTION NOW AVAILABLE IN INEXPENSIVE PAPERBACKS

DIPLOMAT AMONG WARRIORS
By Robert Murphy   N-1130   95¢
The author was Eisenhower's undercover representative during World War II, and was ace troubleshooter for three other Presidents.

A CELLARFUL OF NOISE
By Brian Epstein   R-1200   50¢
The personal story of the man who discovered The Beatles and still guides them today. Sixteen pages of photos.

THE FBI NOBODY KNOWS
By Fred J. Cook   N-1214   95¢
Hard-hitting, no-punches-pulled inside story of our most famous government agency and the man who dominates it. N.Y. Times quote.

INSIDE KU KLUX KLAN
By Paul J. Gillette & Eugene Tillinger   R-1223   50¢
The true story of the Klan—about to undergo Federal investigation—and what it has done to America in the past 100 years.

TO DO JUSTICE
Edited by William Pain   #9000 $1.00
A picture/text history, with award-winning photos, of the heroic struggle for human rights in the United States.

RICHARD BURTON
By Ruth Waterbury   X-1143   60¢
The whole Burton story—from his childhood in Wales to his marriage to Elizabeth Taylor. His only biography in print.

THE NEW LOW CARBOHYDRATE DIET
By William I. Kaufman   P-101 $1.00
The diet that is sweeping the country—with an important new feature—the "Daily Gram Counter" that tells you what to eat and warns you when to stop.

KIND-HEARTED TIGER
By Gilbert Stuart and Alan Levy   T-1174   75¢
The true story of the man they called "The Lawrence of China"—and the days before the United States' entry into war with Japan.

LEGION OF STRANGERS
By Charles Mercer   X-1117   60¢
The story of the most glamorous army of all-time—the French Foreign Legion.

PRINCE OF THIEVES
J. J. Lynx   R-1160   50¢
The incredible story of George Manolesco, audacious amorist and superlative thief. Soon to be a Peter Sellers movie.

NOTE: Pyramid pays postage on orders for 4 books or more. On orders for less than 4 books, add 10¢ per book for postage and handling.

— WHEREVER PAPERBACKS ARE SOLD OR USE THIS COUPON —

PYRAMID BOOKS
Dept. K-141, 444 Madison Avenue, New York, N. Y. 10022
Please send me the NON-FICTION BESTSELLERS circled below. I enclose
$_____

| N-1130 | R-1200 | N-1214 | R-1223 | #9000 |
| X-1143 | P-101 | T-1174 | X-1117 | R-1160 |

Name_____
Street_____
City_____ State_____ Zip_____

The Best of Modern Science Writing
In Inexpensive Paperback Editions

THE WORLDS OF SCIENCE

THE HUMAN BRAIN, John Pfeiffer (Physiology)	WS/1 75¢
MAYA, Charles Gallenkamp (Archaeology)	WS/2 75¢
NINE PLANETS, Alan E. Nourse (Astronomy)	WS/3 75¢
LIVING EARTH, Peter Farb (Biology)	WS/4 65¢
CHEMISTRY CREATES A NEW WORLD, Bernard Jaffe (Chemistry)	WS/5 75¢
THE ROAD TO MAN, Herbert Wendt (Natural History)	WS/6 75¢
GIANTS OF SCIENCE, Philip Cane (General Science)	WS/7 75¢
SNAKES OF THE WORLD, Raymond L. Ditmars (Zoology)	WS/8 75¢
THE ABC OF PHYSICS, Jerome S. Meyer (Physics)	WS/9 75¢
COMPUTERS, Stanley L. Englebardt (Cybernetics)	WS/10 75¢
MAN AND DOLPHIN, John C. Lilly, M.D. (Zoology)	WS/11 75¢
KINGDOM OF THE OCTOPUS, Frank W. Lane (Zoology)	WS/12 75¢
DINOSAURS, Nicholas Hotton III (Paleontology)	WS/13 75¢
THE STORY OF WEATHER, Captain David C. Holmes, U.S.N. (Meteorology)	WS/14 75¢
FACT AND FANCY, Isaac Asimov (General Science)	WS/15 75¢
ELECTRONICS, Stanley L. Englebardt (Electronics)	WS/16 75¢
CONQUEST OF THE MOON, William Hines (Astronautics)	WS/17 75¢
ELEPHANT, L. Sprague de Camp (Natural History)	WS/18 75¢
NEW WORLDS OF OCEANOGRAPHY, Captain E. John Long, U.S.N. (Oceanography)	WS/19 75¢
NEW FRONTIERS IN MEDICINE, Stanley L. Englebardt (Medicine)	WS/20 75¢
THE HUMAN MACHINE, Harry Moody (Biology)	WS/21 75¢

NOTE: Pyramid pays postage on orders for four or more books. On orders for less than four books, add 10¢ per book to cover postage and handling.

WHEREVER PAPERBACKS ARE SOLD OR USE THIS COUPON

PYRAMID BOOKS
Dept. K-142, 444 Madison Avenue, New York, N.Y. 10022

Please send me the WORLDS OF SCIENCE books which I have encircled below. I enclose $_____.

WS/1 WS/2 WS/3 WS/4 WS/5 WS/6 WS/7
WS/8 WS/9 WS/10 WS/11 WS/12 WS/13 WS/14
WS/15 WS/16 WS/17 WS/18 WS/19 WS/20 WS/21

Name_____

Street_____

City_____ State_____ Zip_____